心 灵 的 回 音
POEMS & HYMNS

中英对照世界名诗选译

于中旻 译

河南文艺出版社

图书在版编目(CIP)数据

心灵的回音:英汉对照/(英)莎士比亚等著;于中旻
译. —郑州:河南文艺出版社,2007.12
　　ISBN 978-7-80623-900-1

　　Ⅰ.心⋯　　Ⅱ.①莎⋯②于⋯　　Ⅲ.①英语－汉语－
对照读物②诗歌－作品集－西方国家　　Ⅳ.H319.4:I

　　中国版本图书馆 CIP 数据核字(2007)第 187322 号

出版发行　河南文艺出版社　　　　　　开本 16
本社地址　郑州市鑫苑路18号11栋　　印张 12.25
承印单位　北京宏伟双华印刷有限公司　字数 180000
经销单位　新华书店　　　　　　　　　版次 2007 年 12 月第 1 版
纸张规格　670 毫米×1020 毫米　　　　印次 2007 年 12 月第 1 次印刷
标准书号　ISBN 978-7-80623-900-1　　定价 20.00 元

如发现印装质量问题,请与承印单位联系。

前　言

在世界上不同的文学中,诗的领域发展得最早。中国最早的文学是"击壤歌""卿云歌"和《诗经》;希腊文学的《荷马史诗》(Homer);古巴比伦的《吉尔戈迈士史诗》(Gilgamesh Epic);印度的《摩诃婆罗多史诗》(Mahabharata),都是以诗歌的形式出现。这是由于诗歌能表达情感,易于记忆,便于传诵。早期的诗与歌,是不分开的;而且在咏歌之外,还会手之舞之,足之蹈之。

亚里斯多德(Aristotle)认为,诗歌(包括诗剧),比历史更重要。因为:历史记载的是过去的事,诗歌说到将来可能发生的事;历史是关乎个别的人,诗歌是普遍性的,其所描述的是人性,可以发生在任何个人身上。

《圣经》中早就记载诗歌的教导作用。摩西以诗歌教导以色列的百姓;先知以赛亚、以西结、哈巴谷等,都有诗歌的教导。诗篇中的训诲诗,显然是以教导为目的;其他部分,也是感动造就人,把人的心引向敬拜神,那不仅是圣徒所发的心声,更是诗人受圣灵感动,预言基督的心。至于先知书中的预言,多以诗的形式发出。以后诗人的作品,常使用"灵感"的语词。

诗因为有韵,所以诵读时使人产生美感和快感,同时可以有教育作用,对于思想的传播,比枯燥的理论容易吸引人。

佛教在中国的传播,并不是由于他们玄奥的教义,而是在于其运用浅白的通俗文学。其中的"变文"就是借说书而说教,使听众不知不觉接受到心窝。"变文"的意思是,说一段道白夹一段唱词。在当时,这不仅是普及的娱乐,更有教育的作用。

基督教是歌唱的宗教。奥古斯丁(St. Augustine) 还没有归主,寻求真道的时候,在米兰听安波罗修(St. Ambrosius)主教讲道;安波罗修也是诗人,把他的诗作谱曲以教导会众歌唱,以激励信徒。奥古斯丁说:有时讲道没有进入心中,但是借着不可抵拒的音乐,把歌词从耳朵唱进心里。

诗歌是情感的升华,又具有语词的美,所以诗是文学中的冠冕。

西方文学,基本上是基督教文学;而其杰出的文学作品,则是《圣经》的注脚。特别是在十七世纪以后，英国文学确定了其在西方文学的领导地位：在那个时代，英国出版了主要是廷道勒(William Tyndale, c.1494—1536) 所译的《日内瓦圣经》(1560年)，经过修订后，成为英雅各王钦定译本(1611年)。复有诗人莎士比亚(William Shakespeare,1564—1616)和弥尔顿(John Milton, 1608—1674)。他们不仅在英国文学上空前绝后，在世界文学上也无人可以超越。法国文豪雨果(VictorHugo, 1773—1828) 说得好："英国有两本书：《圣经》和莎士比亚；英国产生了莎士比亚，但《圣经》产生了英国。"

实际上，莎士比亚和弥尔顿都深受《圣经》的影响。廷道勒伟大的天才译笔，不仅把《圣经》中的诗体翻译得美妙无比，而且全本《圣经》读来都像庄严的诗；钦定译本修订时，仍保留了这种风格。弥尔顿的主要诗作《失乐园》(Paradise Lost)、《得乐园》(Paradise Regained) 及《斗士参孙》(Samson Agonistes)，当然都是以《圣经》为主体写成的史诗；莎士比亚写的剧本有三十七个，每剧中都引用《圣经》，平均有二十处以上，并有一百五十四篇Sonnets(十四行诗)，也是取材于《圣经》。就达到了"以娱以教"的目的，把《圣经》原则和信仰，运用于日常生活，真配称为道德的教师。到现在使用英文的人，往往用了他们的成语而不自知。到去查考牛津字典(Oxford English Dictionary) 时，才发现其第一次使用的出处，可见其影响有多么深远了。

1881至1885年，英文修订本在英国问世。有人向司布真(Charles H. Spurgeon)请教他的意见。司布真认为新译本在英文上弱于钦定本。至于以后的译本，更是远落在后面了，原因是当代文学水准的普遍低落。

追想在文艺复兴时代，注重全人教育；意大利的米开朗琪罗(Michelangelo)是著名的艺术家、画家、雕塑家、建筑家，也是诗人。至于教牧中，英国的形式派诗人但恩 (John Donne) 任圣保罗大教堂的主牧；牧师乔治·赫柏特(George Herbert)也以擅长作诗知名，后来约翰·卫斯理(John Wesley)还曾把赫柏特的诗五十余首修订，纳入其圣诗集。凯恩(Thomas Ken)、华慈(Isaac Watts)、纽屯(John Newton)，都是诗人，也都任教职，在聚会中唱他们自己作的圣诗；纽屯还曾与当时的诗人库仆(William Cowper) 合作出版了《俄尼诗集》(Olney Hymns)。其中如凯恩主教(Thomas Ken)的颂诗，自然是出于《圣经》，今天我们教会中普遍唱的"三一颂"竟少人知道其原来面貌，也收在这里。在本集也可能意外看到英国著名的三大浪漫诗人拜伦(George Gordon Byron)、济慈(John Keats)和雪莱(Percy Bysshe Shelly)的作品。虽然他们的信仰说不上纯正，名声少说也算不上好，其中拜伦连他自己也知道是离经叛道，别人更把他看成是敌基督的；但他始终叛离不了《圣经》的传统影响。事实上，这里所收罗的诗歌，作者来自许多不同的行业，其中只有乔治·赫柏特，是以宗教诗人知名，未写过非宗教性的诗。可见西方文学与基督教诗歌关系之深，因为同源于神所启示的宝贵《圣经》。《圣经》成为"诗魂"，了解《圣经》就无法了解西方文化，不能充分享受西方文学。在另一方面，圣经文学是作者表达其对《圣经》的了解，因此，也就能帮助读者了解《圣经》。

华人有"诗如其人"的说法。不过，我以为审评诗的美，像作诗的人一样，有灵、魂、体之分：特别信息是灵，意境超远是魂，辞藻华美是体。如果三者都没有可取的，就真是无足观了。当然，只有《圣经》是最高灵感的源泉，人类诗歌也是因此而达到最高的境界。

说到翻译，几乎没有人不知道严复(几道) 的信、达、雅理论。其实那只是理想，不是可行的原则。就以严先生自己的译作——《群学肄言》来说，就难以说是"达"了。那是哪类书？原来是社会学导论。这样岂不更应"达"得多？何况文字的体裁风格不同，无法达到那理想。例如：医学、法律的书，谁能译到达和雅的地步？应该以信为重。又如《水浒传》和《红楼梦》，如果译成同样风格，或互换其风格，必然读来别有滋味。把马克·吐温的作品用桐城派典雅的古文来译，也将十分别致。在译诗的时候，还得顾及声韵意境。贾岛到京师去，在路上得句"鸟宿池边树，僧推月下门"，思索比拟，不知不觉冲了署理京兆尹韩愈的从骑，被带来究问。韩愈听他说明，说：敲字是矣。这是"推敲"的来源。但在千年以后，还难定论；因为敲字音胜，但在月下僧归禅寺，是回到自己的住处，该用不着敲门；而且深夜敲门，不仅惊飞了树上栖宿的鸟，也破坏了意境，也许应该取静为上。

几年前，试译奥玛四行诗(Rubaiyat of Omar Khayyam)，有一首我译为：

晨鸡才初啼几遍，

已经有人在酒店门前叫喊：

"开门吧，我们要走的路还远，

又谁知此去能不能复还！"

自以为还算过得去。但后来想到荆轲刺秦的时候，朋友给他在易水饯别的歌：

> 风萧萧兮易水寒，
>
> 壮士一去兮不复还！

那是悲壮的声韵。而"凉州曲"有：

> 醉卧沙场君莫笑，
>
> 古来征战几人回！

则是缠绵悲凉，自然不该译为刚音。因此，改译如下：

> 晓鸡才初唱晨光熹微，
>
> 已经有人在酒店门前喊催：
>
> "开门吧，我们要行的路还远，
>
> 又谁知此去能不能复回！"

虽然远不及英译所表达的，但自以为比前译稍好些。这里举例说明，不是诉苦，也无意自我表扬；只是说，译诗不易，如有错失，还望读者包涵，并希指教；并相信原作好得多，难以传译。实在说，翻译就是解释，并不能都恰切地表达原意，在翻译过程中，失去了一部分；不幸，有时失去的还会是精髓，因为无法传神，更无法把文化背景一起搬过来。德莱顿说，最好的文学作品不能翻译，为的是要读者去读原文。译作力求有韵；因为原作都是有韵的，而且无韵的诗，大概少有人能记得上十首，中文如此，何况译作！所以不避困难，选择用韵。

从《圣经》发源的诗歌，是基督教文学的瑰宝。本集所收的，虽然都是短诗，献于读者之前，但盼望能够表现浩瀚的伟大作品之一斑。这些都是由英文翻译的；其中有少数原作是别的欧洲语言，则是由英文译本转译。自知谫陋后学，难以期望达到原作者高深的属灵水平；数年来陆续译出的诗歌，虽参校了不同版本，仍恐舛漏在所难免。因迹寻原作，并行刊出，读者可以参证并欣赏，并欢迎指出错误，以便改正。

于中旻谨识

序

于中旻博士精研中英，为译事高手，且浸淫基督教文学领域有成；年来译诗数百首；《心灵的回音》是由他译作中遴选出来的精品；其中包括莎士比亚、弥尔顿、济慈、雪莱及鲁益师等名家的诗作，可谓千古绝咏，是一册诗的珍馐与飨宴。

"诗言志，歌咏言"，诗是文学中的文学，艺术中的艺术。按说诗是不可以翻译的，必须要读原作才能领会出诗本来的韵味，但透过译者诗意心灵的重组与美妙的译笔，也能将原作的神韵体现出来。于教授为诗坛祭酒，他的译笔，饱蘸了诗思的文采，所传译出来的佳句，自是美不胜收。援引以下几组诗句，与读者共赏：

从深沉的幽暗中　　济慈 John Keats

像从深沉的幽暗中一只银色的鸽子冲上去，

射入东方的光明，

扇动的双翼上负载着欢乐满盈，

你的灵魂也是这样飞入天庭，

那里是永远的爱与和平；

……

圣诞钟声　　朗菲罗 Henry Wadsworth Longfellow

在圣诞节我听到了钟声，

奏出古老熟习的歌颂，

甜美而且激越

在反复的述说

地上有平安,善意归人群!

……

1

夜的颂诗　　　朗菲罗　Henry Wadsworth Longfellow

我听见夜的衣裾

扫过她大理石的殿堂！

我看见她黑貂皮的裙边

镶嵌着天上的星光！

我感觉到她的存在，大能的影响

俯在我以上；

夜平静，庄严的临在

像我所爱的一样。

……

孩子们都已进来了吗？　　　佚名

夜晚临近时我常回想

那一幢老屋建在山上，

那庭院宽广百花绽放

孩子们自由地戏游欢畅。

深黑的夜终于降临，

欢笑也归于低沉，

母亲周围巡视并且说：

"孩子们都已进来了吗？"

……

《心灵的回音》为读者打开了一箱璀璨的珍宝。诗以中英对照刊印，读者可由原诗与译作中窥见于教授的功力，更可以由诗中读出对基督教信仰的执著与丰富的生命信息。

殷　颖

2

目　录

心灵的回音
POEMS & HYMNS

灵魂与肉体

十四行诗 sonnet 146 莎士比亚 William Shakespeare

可怜的灵魂，我罪恶世界的中央，

你受骗去跟那些反叛的势力结帮，

为什么你里面憔悴受苦无量，

外面的墙却油漆得贵价辉煌？

为什么花偌大的代价，租约那么短，

为你那将倾残的巨厦付上许多钱？

内藏的蠹虫，岂不是要蚀尽你

投下的巨款？你肉体岂不也有终点？

灵魂啊，让你的仆役耗费给你生活供养，

要它瘦减，使你的富藏增长，

卖掉无用的时间换取神圣的永约，

外面的富丽壮观全消失，里面却强壮。

　　死亡啮噬人，你啮噬死亡也是这样，

　　到死亡死去了，然后不再有死亡。

Poor soul, the centre of my sinful earth,

My sinful earth, these rebel powers that thee array,

Why dost thou pine within and suffer dearth,

Painting thy outward walls so costly gay?

Why so large cost, having so short a lease,

Dost thou upon thy fading mansion spend?

Shall worms, inheritors of this excess,

Eat up thy charge? Is this thy body's end?

Then, soul, live thou upon thy servant's loss,

And let that pine to aggravate thy store.

Buy terms divine in selling hours of dross,

Within be fed, without be rich no more.

    So shalt thou feed on Death, that feeds on men,

    And Death once dead, there's no more dying then.

死亡，你不要骄狂

约翰·但恩 John Donne

死亡，你不要骄狂！虽然有些人称你
　　强大而且可怕，但你并不是那样；
　　因为有的人你以为已经打倒胜过了，
却没有死；可怜的死亡，你也杀不了我。
从安息和睡眠，可以看见你的影像，
　　而且，更要从你流出多少欢畅；
　　当我们最好的人与你同往，
他们的骸骨安息了，灵魂得到释放。
你是奴隶，服事命运，机会，君王和流浪汉，
　　是毒药，战争，疾病的内涵；
　　罂粟或迷药也可以使我们有好的睡眠，
而且强过你的本事。那么，你有什么好神气？
　　在短暂的睡眠过后，我们永远复起，
　　死亡就不再有了。死亡，你定要死。

Death, be not proud, though some have called thee

   Mighty and dreadful, for thou are not so;

   For those whom thou think＇st thou dost overthrow

Die not, poor Death, Nor yet canst thou kill me.

From rest and sleep, which but thy picture be,

   Much pleasure – then from thee much more must flow;

   And soonest our best men with thee do go,

Rest of their bones and soul＇s delivery.

Thou＇rt slave to fate, chance, kings, and desperate men,

   And doth with poison, war, and sickness dwell;

   And poppy or charms can make us sleep as well,

And better than thy stroke. Why swell＇st thou then?

   One short sleep past, we wake eternally,

   And death shall be no more. Death, thou shalt die.

华冠

乔治·赫柏特

George Herbert

一个花环的冠冕配得的颂赞，

颂赞是你配得的我向你呈献，

我献给你，你知我所有道路，

我生活的道路就是弯弯曲曲，

实是死的，不是活：因生命是正直，

像一条直线，永远引向你，

向你，你远超过诈欺，

超越诈欺似乎胜于朴实。

求赐我朴实，我就能活出，

活出并像你，我就知你道路，

知道并遵行：我就能呈献，

用这贫乏花环，献你颂赞冠冕。

A wreathed garland of deserved praise,

Of praise deserved, unto thee I give,

I give to thee, who knowest all my ways,

My crooked winding ways, wherein I live,

Wherein I die, not live: for life is straight,

Straight as a line, and ever tends to thee,

To thee, who art more far above deceit,

Than deceit seems above simplicity.

Give me simplicity, that I may live,

So live and like, that I may know thy ways,

Know them and practise them: then shall I give

For this poor wreath, give thee a crown of praise.

升轮*

乔治·赫柏特
George Herbert

当上帝造人之初，
有一只福杯在他旁边；
他说：让我们尽量的倾注给他；
让世界的丰盛散布周边，
　　成为两间的系连。

这样，他先赐下能力；
随后是美，又加才智，荣耀，欢喜。
当几乎要倾尽时，上帝稍事停息，
看到他唯一的至宝
　　**余存，安息在杯底。

他说，如果我连
这珍宝也赐给我所造的，
他就会舍我而崇拜恩赐，
安息于自然，而非自然的主宰，
　　这样，二者将同归丧失。

让他得着其余的，
得着那些，也怨叹而无安息；
使他富而不足，且有困疲，至少
如果仁慈不能引他，困疲
　　会举起他到我怀里。

（* 升轮，或名滑车，吊杆。　** 余存、安息，均为 rest 。）

8

When God at first made man,

Having a glass of blessings standing by,

"Let us" (said he) "pour on him all we can:

Let the world's riches, which dispersed lie,

Contract into a span."

So strength first made a way;

Then beauty flow'd, then wisdom, honour, pleasure:

When almost all was out, God made a stay,

Perceiving that alone of all his treasure

Rest in the bottom lay.

"For if I should" (said he)

"Bestow this jewel also on my creature,

He would adore my gifts instead of me,

And rest in Nature, not the God of Nature:

So both should losers be."

"Yet let him keep the rest,

But keep them with repining restlessness;

Let him be rich and weary, that at least,

If goodness lead him not, yet weariness

May toss him to my breast."

爱

乔治·赫柏特 George Herbert (1593–1633)

爱上前来欢迎我。但我的灵魂缩退
蒙着歉疚的尘灰和罪。
可是，明眼的爱，从我一迈进门槛，
就看出我的迟疑不前。
爱更加靠近我跟前，温柔亲切地
问我有什么缺欠。

我说："一位贵宾要来这里。"
爱说："那人正是你。"
"啊呀！我？这样的忘恩负义，一无良善？
我不敢看你的脸。"
爱拉着我的手，微笑着回应：
"除了我还有谁造人的眼睛？"

"主啊，不错。但我污损了双眼，理当抱羞
去到该去的那里。"
爱说道："你可知道是谁背负了愆尤？"
"亲爱的，我愿意来服事。"
爱说道："你一定要入席，来尝我的肉。"
这样，我就坐下来享受。

10

Love   George Herbert

Love bade me welcome; yet my soul drew back

Guilty of dust and sin.

But quick—ey' d Love, observing me grow slack

From my first entrance in,

Drew nearer to me, sweetly questioning

If I lack' d any thing.

"A guest", I answer' d, "worthy to be here."

Love said, "You shall be he."

"I the unkind, ungrateful? Ah my dear,

I cannot look on thee."

Love took my hand, and smiling did reply,

"Who made the eyes but I?"

"Truth Lord,but I have marr' d them; let my shame

Go where it doth deserve."

"And know you not", says Love, "who bore the blame?"

"My dear, then I will serve."

"You must sit down", says Love, "and taste my meat."

So I did sit and eat.

死亡的最后胜利

塞利 James Shirley

我们所有出身和身分的光荣
　　只是影儿，并没有实质；
没有能够抵御定命的武器，
　　死亡冰冷的手攫住君王；
　　皇冠和权杖
　　必然跌落地上，
同卑贱的弯镰和锄头
在尘土里平等一样。

有人用刀剑收获了土地，
　　种植新的胜利在杀伤的地方；
但他们强壮的勇力至终也得投降，
　　虽然他们仍然互相争狠斗强，
　　或早或是迟
　　向定命屈膝，
必须交出微弱的气息，
作了苍白的俘虏，匍匐去就死。

华冠枯萎在你的眉峰，
　　不能再夸耀你的伟绩丰功；
现在，死亡紫色的祭坛上，
　　得胜者作了流血的牺牲！
　　所有的元首都要去
　　下到幽冷的坟墓，
唯有义人的行为显彰
在尘土中开花吐露芬芳。

注：据说，此诗曾使英国权倾一时的执政者克伦威尔"心头生凉"。

The glories of our birth and state

    Are shadows, not substantial things;

There is no armor against fate,

    Death lays his icy hands on kings;

    Sceptre and crown

    Must tumble down,

And in the dust be equal made

With the poor crooked scythe and spade.

Some men with swords may reap the field,

    And plant fresh laurels where they kill;

But their strong nerves at last must yield,

    They tame but one another still;

    Early or late

    They stoop to fate,

And must give up their murmuring breath,

When they, pale captives, creep to death.

The garlands wither on your brow,

    Then boast no more your mighty deeds;

Upon death's purple altar, now,

    See where the victor victim bleeds!

    All heads must come

    To the cold tomb,

Only the actions of the just

Smell sweet, and blossom in the dust.

注：　(These verses are said to have "hilled the heart" of Oliver Cromwell)

诗人的祈求

弥尔顿 John Milton

正直清洁的心超过所有的殿，

教导我，因为你知道；在万有之先

就在那里，以你大能的翅膀伸展

如同鸽子孵育在广大无边的深渊

使它孕生：我里面有什么黑暗

光照，有什么低贱提升并救援；

为这伟大高远的论辩

使我能正确宣示永恒的计划

证明神的道路在人间。

And chiefly Thou O Spirit, that does prefer

Before all Temples th' upright heart and pure,

Instruct me, for Thou know' st; Thou from the first

Wast present, and with mighty wings outspread

Dove—like satst brooding on the vast Abyss

And mad' st it pregnant: What in me is dark

Illumine, what is low raise and support;

That to the highth of this great Argument

I may assert Eternal Providence,

And justify the ways of God to men.

    From Paradise Lost

当我思量

十四行诗 sonnet19

弥尔顿 John Milton

当我思量我的光如何耗完，
　　进入黑暗无边的世界，还未到中年，
　　而且埋藏才干的人是该死的罪愆，
　　怀才莫展，虽然我心魂深愿
要事奉造我的主，以后在他面前
　　交账，免得在他再临遭责受谴：
　　"神怎要求白昼工作而不给化日光天"，
　　我想要质问；但忍耐阻拦
那样的抱怨，立即回答："神并不需要
　　人的工作或他的才干；最善
　　负他轻省的轭的人，事奉最完善；他权威
尊严。急速遵行他差遣的盈千累万
　　遍布于洋海陆地工作不倦；
　　但也有的只是侍立和随伴。"

When I consider how my light is spent

Ere half my days, in this dark world and wide,

And that one Talent which is death to hide,

Lodg' d with me useless, though my soul more bent

To serve therewith my Maker, and present

My true account, Lest he returning chide;

"Doth God exact day–labour, light denied,"

I fondly ask; But Patience to prevent

That murmur, soon replies,　"God doth not need

Either man' s work or his own gifts; who best

Bear his mild yoke, they serve Him best; His State

Is Kingly. Thousands at his bidding speed

　　And post o' er Land and Ocean without rest;

　　They also serve who only stand and wait."

春天随着冬天

布莱斯翠 Ann Bradstreet

春天来到随着冬天已往
赤裸的树木着上新叶的衣裳,
全黑的大地穿了绿色。
欢欣迎接着普照的阳光。
我的太阳回归有医治的翅膀,
我的灵魂和身体同时欢畅,
我的心昂扬赞美歌唱
因他听了我的哀声和悲伤。
我的冬天已过,我的风暴消逝,
从前的乌云现在也尽都逃避,
即使会再有重来的阴翳,
我将投奔我救援之地。
我有一庇护所可御风暴,
荫蔽处躲避那眩晕的热潮,
我能够进到他的宝座,
他是那位神伟大奇妙。
噢,你成就了我的旅程
美好,晴朗,而且愉快欢喜,
赐福我从幼年直到老年时,
流泪谷成为了泉源洋溢。
噢,我应当做的是殷勤敬虔
欢乐的尽责事奉在主面前;
所有我能给的原是你的
最多还不值一文小钱。

As spring the winter doth succeed

And leaves the naked trees do dress,

The earth all black is clothed in green.

At sunshine each their joy express.

My sun's returned with healing wings,

My soul and body doth rejoice,

My heart exults and praises sings

To Him that heard my wailing voice.

My winter's past, my storms are gone,

And former clouds seem now all fled,

But if they must eclipse again,

I'll run where I was succored.

I have a shelter from the storm,

A shadow from the fainting heat,

I have access to His throne,

Who is a God so wondrous great.

O hath thou made my pilgrimage

Thus pleasant, fair, and good,

Blessed me in youth and elder age,

My Baca* made a springing flood.

O studious am what I shall do

To show my duty with delight;

All I can give is but thine own

And at most a simple mite.

我家失火

布莱斯翠 Ann Bradstreet

1666 年 7 月 10 日

在静夜里我已经安息上床，
却不知祸患就在附近隐藏。
我惊觉听到了如雷的巨响，
夹杂着惨叫的可怕声浪：
"火！" "火啊！" 喊声充满惊惶，
谁也不会想那是我的愿望。

我，立即起来，看见了火光，
我心向着我的上帝求诉：
"在苦难中求你赐给我力量，
不要撇下我无靠无助！"
到外面以后，立即看见，
烈焰吞噬了我的住处。

当我不能够继续看下去，
就称颂主的名，他赏赐又收取，
我积存的财物现在成为虚无，
那本是尘土应该归于尘土。
那全是属于主，并不是我的，
绝不该有任何的抱怨诉苦。

July 10th, 1666

In silent night when rest I took,

For sorrow near I did not look,

I waken'd was with thundring noise

And piteous shreiks of dreadful voice.

That fearful sound of "Fire!" and "Fire!"

Let no man know is my Desire.

I, starting up, the light did spye,

And to my God my heart did cry

To strengthen me in my Distresse,

And not to leave me succourlesse.

Then coming out, beheld apace

The flame consume my dwelling place.

And when I could no longer look,

I blest his Name that gave and took,

That layd my goods now in the dust:

Yea so it was, and so 'twas just.

It was his own: it was not mine;

Far be it that I should repine.

Upon The Burning of Our House

他虽然可能把一切尽都剥夺，
却留下部分足够我们生活。
我忧伤的眼睛也曾经瞥视，
当我常从那废墟边经过：
从这里和那里熟悉的角落，
我常在这里坐，常在那里躺卧。

这里放过我的箱，那里是我的柜，
里面存放着我最宝贵喜欢，
我喜爱的东西都化为灰烬，
我再也不能得以看见。
在你屋顶下再没有宾客的座位，
也不能再在你的桌旁聚集共餐。

再也不能述说那可爱的故事，
再也不能追忆那古老的事情。
灯光不再照耀在你的当中，
也不会听见新郎的欢声。
你将在那里长卧安静，
再见，再见，一切的虚荣。

然后我得着力量责备我的心，
你岂是积攒财宝在地上？
你岂是在腐土上注定你的希望？

22

He might of All justly bereft,

But yet sufficient for us left.

When by the Ruines oft I past,

My sorrowing eyes aside did cast,

And here and there the places spye

Where oft I sate, and long did lye.

Here stood that Trunk, and there that chest;

There lay that store I counted the best:

My pleasant things in ashes lye,

And them behold no more shall I.

Under my roof no guest shall sitt,

Nor at thy Table eat a bitt.

No pleasant tale shall e' er be told,

Nor things recounted done of old.

No candle e' er shall shine in Thee,

Nor bridegroom' s voice e' er heard shall bee.

In silence ever shalt thou lye;

Adeiu, Adeiu; All' s vanity.

Then streight I' gan my heart to chide:

And did thy wealth on earth abide?

Didst fix thy hope on mouldring dust,

你岂是要倚靠血肉的臂膀？
举起你的思想超越青天，
那粪堆的迷雾全消逝净光。

在上面你有一座房屋，
经营建造的是那位大能的工师，
并且有荣美华丽的陈设装饰，
地上的房屋过去它却永远坚立。
那屋已经买定了并且已付清，
是那位万有的主他成全备齐。

其代价是那么巨大超乎所想，
但靠他的恩赐，你拥有安享。
那里的财富满足，我一无所缺；
去吧，我的钱财！去吧，我的宝藏！
这世界不再是我所爱慕，
我的盼望和财宝全在天上。

The arm of flesh didst make thy trust?

Raise up thy thoughts above the skye,

That dunghill mists away may flie.

Thou hast an house on high erect,

Fram' d by that mighty Architect,

With glory richly furnished,

Stands permanent though this bee fled.

It' s purchased, and paid for, too,

By Him who hath enough to doe.

A Prise so vast as is unknown,

Yet, by his Gift, is made thine own.

There' s wealth enough, I need no more;

Farewell my Pelf, farewell my Store.

The world no longer let me Love,

My Hope and Treasure lyes Above.

传扬福音

贝克斯特 Richard Baxter

主呼召我出去工作趁着白天；
警告可怜的灵魂转回切莫迟延：
决心尽快去传播主的道，
随学随教导同安波罗修一般。
时时想到我不能活得长久，
心中火热为得人灵魂争战。
我讲道，不确知是否能再讲，
像将亡的人传给将亡的人！
啊，传道者该如何切望得人悔改，
谁知道教堂与墓园原是比邻？
看到人在传讲，在听，在死亡，
转眼从时间进入无尽的永恒！

This called me out to work while it was day;

And warn poor souls to turn without delay:

Resolving speedily thy Word to preach,

With Ambrose I at once did learn and teach.

Still thinking I had little time to live,

My fervent heart to win men's souls did strive.

I preach as never sure to preach again,

And as a dying man to dying men!

O how should preachers men's repenting crave

Who see how near the Church is to the grave?

And see that while we preach and hear, we die,

Rapt by swift time to vast eternity!

冠冕

马卫勒 Andrew Marvell

当那荆棘冠冕的刺，太长，
　　　加冕在我救主的头上，
　　　造成许多的创伤，
我长愿欲，设法做个华冠为错误补偿：
　　　找遍每个花园，每片草场
采集花朵(我的结果不过有花)
　　　拆毁所有芳香的花塔，
一度曾为我的牧羊女装饰头发。
现在我倾所有的存积
　　　妄想(是我在自欺)
　　　如此丰美的花环编织
荣耀的王所戴的冠冕无一能及；
　　　啊呀！我发现那古蛇仇敌
　　　盘绕着它斑点的胸皮，
　　　弯曲伪装作类似的花枝，
　　　卷缠着名声和利益。
啊！愚人，必朽的荣耀难以久远
将要贬抑属天的皇冠！
但只有你能制伏那古蛇，
解脱它狡猾的结，
断开它所有网罗曲折；
或同时破碎我的奇心淫妄
让这些都凋残，它也就死亡，
虽然用上技巧，选择复营想；
这样，当你践踏两重的战利品，
作足下的冠冕，虽不配冠冕在你头上。

When for the Thorns with which I long, too long,

    With many a piercing wound

    My Saviour's head have crown'd,

I seek with Garlands to redress that Wrong,

    Through every Garden, every Mead

I gather flow'rs (my fruits are only flow'rs)

    Dismantling all the fragrant Towers

That once adorn'd my Shepherdess's head.

And now when I have summ'd up all my store,

    Thinking (so I my self deceive)

    So rich a Chaplet thence to weave

As never yet the king of Glory wore,

    Alas I find the Serpent old

    That, twining in his speckled breast,

    About the flow'rs disguis'd does fold,

    With wreaths of Fame and Interest.

Ah, foolish Man, that would'st debase with them

And mortal Glory, Heaven's Diadem!

But thou who only could'st the Serpent tame,

Either his slipp'ry knots at once untie,

And disentangle all his winding Snare;

Or shatter too with him my curious frame

And let these wither, so that he may die,

Though set with Skill and chosen out with Care;

That they, while Thou on both their Spoils dost tread,

May crown thy Feet, that could not crown thy Head.

人

文涵 Henry Vaughan

思量，坚定和庄严
属于些低级的物住在下世间，
鸟儿像警醒的时钟
　　记认着无声的日子和时间更换，
蜂群在夜里归返蜂巢和花丛
　　知道早，也知道晚，
随太阳醒起，也在同一房舍栖眠；

　　我说，但愿我的神也肯
　　赐给人像这些物的坚定！因他们
　　对他的圣命谨守忠贞，
　　并没有新事务破坏他们的和平；
　　飞鸟不种不收，却有餐有食，
　　花儿活着并没有衣，
　　连所罗门王也不曾有他们的美饰。
人却一直有烦扰，有思虑，
他没有根，也不系定一处，
永不会安息也没有规律
　　在地上奔劳往返来去，
他知道有个家，却说不上在哪里
　　他说，是那么遥远
以至他忘却怎寻觅回家的路。

　　他叩遍每个门户，迷失又流浪，
　　有些顽石的智慧竟比人还强，
　　造物主赐磁石内在的感应，
　　在极暗的黑夜指向家乡；
　　人是一只梭，往返寻觅，
　　经过机杼间来复不已
　　神命定动作，但却未命定安息。

Weighing the steadfastness and state

Of some mean things which here below reside,

Where birds like watchful Clocks the noiseless date

    And Intercourse of Times divide,

Where bees at night get home and hive, and flow' rs

    Early, as well as late,

Rise with the sun, and set in the same bow' rs;

    I would (said I) my God would give

The staidness of these things to man! for these

To his divine appointments ever cleave,

    And no new business breaks their peace;

The birds nor sow, nor reap, yet sup and dine,

    The flow' rs without clothes live,

Yet Solomon was never dressed so fine.

Man hath still either toys, or Care,

He hath no root, nor to one place is tied,

But ever restless and Irregular

    About this earth doth run and ride,

He knows he hath a home, but scarce knows where,

    He says it is so far

That he hath quite forgot how to go there.

    He knocks at all doors, strays and roams,

Nay hath not so much wit as some stones have,

Which in the darkest night point to their homes,

    By some hid sense their Maker gave;

Man is the shuttle, to whose winding quest

    And passage through these looms

God ordered motion, but ordained no rest.

Man

世界

文涵 Henry Vaughan

1
那夜晚我看见了永恒
如同一个大环有无尽的光而且洁净，
全然无声，它也是光明，
在它下面，时间以小时，日，年
　　受天体驱动
像个巨大的影子运行，这世界
和它的长尾跟从前冲；
迷恋的爱人以他们精巧的作风
在作态怨诉，
他的竖琴，他的幻想，他的奔逐，
小聪明的低下欢娱，
同着手套，爱情结，愚昧的网罗爱欲
他可贵的财富
全都散置不顾，他的双目
只向那朵花儿倾注。

2
那阴沉的政客挂着庄重和苦脸
像午夜的浓雾移动得那么缓慢
他不就去，也不流连；
蹙着眉，可定罪的意念(晦暗像日蚀般)
　　在他的灵魂间，
如云的见证哀哭在外面
追着他一致呐喊。
却如地鼠钻营，他用的方法
　　是在地下做工，
攫取他的猎物，但隐住
他的阴谋，
利用教会和祭坛肥己，
　　作假看如微物，
周围是泣血和泪雨，
但他饮下不顾。

1

I saw eternity the other night
Like a great Ring of pure and endless light,
All calm, as it was bright,
And round beneath it, Time in hours, days, years
     Driv' n by the spheres
Like a vast shadow moved, In which the world
And all her train were hurled;
The doting Lover in his quaintest strain
Did there Complain,
Near him, his Lute, his fancy, and his flights,
Wits sour delights,
With gloves, and knots the silly snares of pleasure
Yet his dear Treasure
All scattered lay, while his eyes did pour
Upon a flow' r.

2

The darksome Statesman hung with weights and woe
Like a thick midnight—fog moved there so slow
He did not stay, nor go;
Condemning thoughts (like sad Eclipses) scowl
  Upon his soul,
And Clouds of crying witnesses without
Pursued him with one shout.
Yet digged the Mole, and lest his ways be found
  Worked under ground,
Where he did Clutch his prey, but one did see
  That policy,
Churches and altars fed him, Perjuries
  Were gnats and flies,
It rained about him blood and tears, but he
Drank them as free.

3

害怕的吝啬鬼坐在铜锈堆，
一生在那里苦思憔悴，
不信任自己的手去碰那尘灰，
却不肯积一点在上面，
　　宁活着担心盗贼。
有千万人像他一样的颠倒
各人拥抱自己的阿堵物，
彻底的伊庇鸠鲁，天堂是感官肚腹
　　讥笑虚饰
也有人放纵无节制
　　并不斤斤论理；
有软弱的人纤细必计，为小器奴役
　　却自炫耀得意，
可怜的真理被藐视，坐着详记
　　他们的胜利。

4

另有些人，一直在哭泣和歌唱，
歌唱，哭泣，升达天上，
　　进入那环，虽然不用翅膀。
噢，傻人哪(我说)，宁喜欢暗夜
　　却不要真光，
生活在洞穴中，恨恶白昼
　　因为能显明道路，
那道路从死亡和幽暗的住处
　　引领到神那里去，
那道路使你能踏向太阳，
　　比它还要明亮。
但是当我这样论说他们的痴狂
　　有一位向我轻声讲：
那环新郎不是给别人预备的
　　只为他的新娘。

> 凡世界上的一切事，就像肉体的情欲，眼目的情欲，并今生的骄傲，都不是从父来的，乃是从世界来的。这世界和其上的情欲，都要过去，唯独遵行神旨意的，是永远长存。
>
> 约壹二：16,17

34

3

The fearful miser on a heap of rust
Sat pining all his life there, did scarce trust
His own hands with the dust,
Yet would not place one piece above, but lives
    In fear of thieves.
Thousands there were as frantic as himself
And hugged each one his pelf,
The down−right Epicure placed heav' n in sense
    And scorned pretence
While others slipt into a wide Excess
    Said little less;
The weaker sort slight, trivial wares Enslave
    Who think them brave,And poor, despised
truth sat Counting by
    Their victory.

4

Yet some, who all this while did weep and sing,
And sing, and weep, soared up into the Ring,
    But most would use no wing.
O fools (said I,) thus to prefer dark night
    Before true light,
To live in grots, and caves, and hate the day
    Because it shows the way,
The way which from this dead and dark abode
    Leads up to God,
A way where you might tread the Sun, and be
    More bright than he.
But as I did their madness so discuss
    One whispered thus,
This Ring the Bridegroom did for none provide
    But for his bride.

圣书

文涵 Henry Vaughan

永恒的上帝！创造一切
生活在这里，为堕落的人；
万古磐石！在你荫下
茫茫众生繁长又消逝。
你早已认识这纸，当它
仅是种子，以后发长成草；
它用不着穿衣，也不纺线，
却做成细麻布，给人蔽体；
你知道他们的生命，思想行动举止
或是好麦子，或是稗子不结实。

你早已认识这树，还在绿荫下
被覆庇，使它成为荫庇。
他滋生，发展，长起，
像是永存不会死。
你早已认识这无害的牲畜，
照你的定旨生活饮食，
吃各样的青物；然后饱足眠息，
它穿过的毛皮，现在铺展开，
成了这古老书帙的外衣。
这使我慧悟哭泣，看到
灰尘的自己；只不过是灰尘，
论干净还不能与灰尘相比。
你早已认识，已看见这一切，
还未成形前，你已认识我们现在的体质。

噢，全知，荣耀的灵！
你使树木牲畜更新，使人复起，
你叫万事复兴，
却只毁灭痛苦和死，
那些爱你，寻求你面的，
为你工作的必蒙赏赐！

36

Eternal God! Maker of all
That have lived here, since the man's fall;
The Rock of ages! in whose shade
They live unseen, when here they fade.
Thou knew'st this paper, when it was
Mere seed, and after that but grass;
Before 'twas drest or spun, and when
Made linen, who did wear it then:
What were their lives, their thoughts and deeds
Whether good corn, or fruitless weeds.

   Thou knew'st this Tree, when a green shade
Covered it, since a Cover made,
And where it flourished, grew and spread,
As if it never should be dead.
   Thou knew'st this harmless beast, when he
Did live and feed by thy decree
On each green thing; then slept (well fed)
Clothed with this skin, which now lies spread
A Covering o'er this aged book,
Which makes me wisely weep and look
On my own dust; mere dust it is,
But not so dry and clean as this.
Thou knew'st and saw'st them all and though
Now scattered thus, dost know them so.

   O knowing, glorious Spirit! when
Thou shalt restore trees, beasts and men,
When thou shalt make all new again,
Destroying only death and pain,
Give him amongst thy works a place,
Who in them loved and sought thy face!

醒起，我的灵魂

肯恩 Thomas Ken

醒起，我的灵魂，同着白日
尽每天的责任自强不息：
洒脱懒散，欢乐兴起
去献上清晨的祭。

兴起，我的心啊，你要举起
尽你本分同众天使一样，
他们日夜不倦地歌唱
颂扬那永远的王。

所有颂赞归保守我的主，
当安眠时使我得以更新：
主啊，当我从死里复起
与永远生命有分。

主啊，我向你再次的祈求；
使我罪消散如向日晨露；
所新发出的心思意念
你在我心灵充足。

这一天指引，管理，引导我，
一切的计划，言语，行动，
所有我的智能和力量，
都是为荣耀你名。

赞美真神万福之源，
天下万民都当颂扬；
天使天军齐颂主名：
颂赞圣父圣子圣灵。

38

Awake, my soul, and with the sun
Thy daily stage of duty run:
Shake off dull sloth, and joyful rise
To pay thy morning sacrifice.

Wake, and lift up thyself, my heart,
And with the angels bear thy part,
Who all night long unwearied sing
High praise to the eternal King.

All Praise to Thee, who safe has kept,
And hast refreshed me while I slept:
Grant, Lord, when I from death shall wake
I may of endless life partake.

Lord, I my vows to Thee renew;
Disperse my sins as morning dew;
Guard my first spring of thought and will,
And with Thyself my spirit fill.

Direct, control, suggest, this day,
All I design, or do, or say,
That all my powers, with all their might,
In Thy sole glory may unite.

Praise God, from whom all blessings flow,
Praise Him,all creatures here below,
Praise Him above, ye heavenly host,
Praise Father, Son, and Holy Ghost.

我的神，荣耀归于你

肯恩 Thomas Ken

我的神，荣耀归于你，今夜
为光中所有福分感谢你赏赐；
求保守我，啊，万王之王，
你全能翅膀覆翼。

主啊，因你的爱子赦免我，
今天所犯下的一切过失，
在我睡前能够有和平，
对神，世人，和自己。

教导我生活，使我不怕死
看坟墓不过是我的眠床；
教导我死亡，使我能在
可畏大日进荣耀里。

啊，我的灵魂在你得安息，
进入甜美睡眠眼睛闭上，
安睡为了要再起来时
服事神更有力量。

如果我夜里不能够入睡，
赐给我灵魂属天的思想，
不让恶梦扰乱我安息，
或黑暗权势侵害。

赞美真神万福之源，
天下万民都当颂扬，
天使天军齐颂主名，
赞美圣父圣子圣灵。

Glory to Thee, my God, this night
For all the blessings of the light;
Keep me, O keep me, King of Kings,
Beneath Thy own almighty wings.

Forgive me, Lord, for Thy dear Son,
The ill that I this day has done,
That with the world, myself, and Thee
I, ere I sleep, at peace may be.

Teach me to live, that I may dread
The grave as little as my bed;
Teach me to die, that so I may
Rise glorious at the awful day.

O may my soul on Thee repose,
And with sweet sleep mine eyelids close,
Sleep that may me more vigorous make
To serve my God when I awake.

When in the night I sleepless lie,
My soul with heavenly thoughts supply;
Let no ill dreams disturb my rest,
No powers of darkness me molest.

Praise God, from whom all blessings flow,
Praise Him, all creatures here below,
Praise Him above, ye heavenly host,
Praise Father, Son and Holy Ghost.

盲童

奚波 Colley Cibber

噢，说什么东西叫作光，
　　我一向不能够分享？
眼光又是怎样的幸福美好，
　　噢，说给你可怜的瞎孩子知道。

你说起美妙的东西你能看得清，
　　你说太阳的照耀光明；
虽然我感觉得到他的温暖，
　　但他怎能造成黑夜和白天？

安排昼和夜的是我自己，
　　在于我睡觉或是游戏；
如果我保持常醒不眠，
　　对于我那就永远是白天。

我常听到你们的长叹声，
　　惋惜我的忧患不幸；
不过我确能够忍耐坚持，
　　我从不曾知道的损失。

无法得到的请不要告诉我
　　免得破坏我心灵的欢乐：
因此，每当我能够歌唱，
　　我是个瞎孩子，我是君王。

O, say what is that thing called Light,

   Which I must ne' er enjoy?

What are the blessings of the sight,

   O, tell your poor blind boy!

You talk of wondrous things you see,

   You say the sun shines bright;

I feel him warm, but how can he

   Or make it day or night?

My day or night myself I make

   Whene' er I sleep or play;

And could I ever keep awake

   With me ' t were always day.

With heavy sighs I often hear

   You mourn my hapless woe;

But sure with patience I can bear

   A loss I ne' er can know.

Then let not what I cannot have

   My cheer of mind destroy:

Whilst thus I sing, I am a king,

   Although a poor blind boy.

The Blind Boy

垂死的基督徒对他的灵魂

坡仆 Alexander Pope

属天火焰的生之火花！
离去，噢，脱离这必死的躯壳！
颤抖，希望，缠绵，飞逝，
噢！这痛苦，这死的福乐！
停息，爱生的本性，停息你的争持，
让我消萎进入生命里！

听啊！他们在轻语：天使们说，
灵魂姐妹，离开吧！
是什么完全吞没了我？
取去了我的官感，关闭了我的视象，
淹没了我的心灵，吸竭了我的气息？
告诉我，我的灵魂，难道这就是死亡？

世界退去了；它消逝了！
天堂展现在我眼前！我的双耳
听到撒拉弗的声响！
借我，借你的翅膀！我乘驾！我飞翔！
坟墓啊！你得胜的权势在哪里？
死亡啊！你的毒钩在哪里？

*末两句出自哥林多前书（圣经 15 章 55 节）

Vital spark of heavenly flame!

Quit, O quit this mortal frame!

Trembling, hoping, lingering, flying,

O! the pain, the bliss of dying!

Cease, fond nature, cease thy strife,

And let me languish into life!

Hark! they whisper: angels say,

Sister spirit, come away!

What is this absorbs me quite?

Steals my senses, shuts my sight,

Drowns my spirit, draws my breath?

Tell me, my soul, can this be death?

The world recedes; it disappears!

Heaven opens on my eyes! my ears

With sounds seraphic ring!

Lend, lend your wings! I mount! I fly!

O Grave! where is thy victory?

O Death! where is thy sting?*

*The last two lines are from I Corinthians, 15:55

无信仰者得势

德怀特 Timothy Dwight

这里站着假冒伪善者穿着暗褐衣衫，
一副安息日的面孔还带着皱眉苦脸。
他说着现今这阴暗时代的故事阴暗，
这个可哀世界充满着最可哀的罪犯；
皱纹的面颊上为别人的罪流着眼泪，
对他里面的地狱就把眼睛闭上不看。

那边是圆滑的圣职人员常挂着笑颜，
怕伤害罪人心，地狱的警告他讲不惯。
可怕的事情总沾不着他温和的舌边，
刺耳的真理会对高贵良善的人冒犯。
那奇异的"重生"，那循理派的"恩典"，
在他的心中，在他讲章里，都难以发现。
柏拉图美好的故事他倒笨拙地讲演，
陈腐的，炉边谈，道德剧，古板而可厌；
能够下地狱的罪愆，救赎大爱的赦免，
在他的基督和圣经里面都是那样遥远。
他说，人类应该停止犯罪那是最好不过，
如此就会有好的声誉；内心也就有真平安。
他自然知道向上心不能驱使如此作，
但盼望他们仍然会乐于上到天堂。
每个礼拜他总不忘尽责任去作探访，
巧言，滑稽，大笑；把私人的新闻重复传讲；
各样烟熏的美食，对她的奶酪欣赏，
给她点着烟斗，并且把婴孩抱在手上。
或住在大的城市里，穿着漆亮的皮鞋，
修整的假发，合身长衣，闪光的紧裤，
他躬身，谈论政治，学礼仪举止温和；
最恭谨的询问，最温雅流畅的笑语；
富人谐语时高声大笑，恭维讲的故事；
对夫人们的时装，注目，注目，再注目；
烹调精妙的火鸡餐最适口美味果腹；

Here stood Hypocrisy, in sober brown,
His sabbath face all sorrow'd with a frown.
A dismal tale he told of dismal times,
And this sad world brimfull of saddest crimes;
Furrowed his cheeks with tears for others' s in,
But closed his eyelids on the hell within.

There smiled the smooth Divine, unused to wound
The sinner' s heart with hell' s alarming sound.
No terrors on his gentle tongue attend,
No grating truths the nicest ear offend.
That strange "New Birth" , that methodistic "Grace"
Nor in his heart, nor sermons, found a place.
Plato' s fine tales he clumsily retold,
Trite, fireside, moral see-saws, dull as old;
His Christ and Bible placed at good remove
Guilt hell-deserving, and forgiving love.
Twas best, he said, mankind should cease to sin;
Good fame required it; so did peace within.
Their honours, well he knew, would ne' er be driven;
But hoped they still would please to go to heaven.
Each week, he paid his visitation dues;
Coaxed, jested, laughed; rehearsed the private news;

Smoked with each goody, thought her cheese excelled;
Her pipe he lighted, and her baby held.
Or placed in some great town, with lacquered shoes,
Trim wig, and trimmer gown, and glistening hose,
He bowed, talked politics, learned manners mild;
Most meekly questioned, and most smoothly smiled;
At rich men' s jests laughed loud, their stories praised;
Their wives' new patterns gazed, and gazed, and gazed;
Most daintily on pampered turkeys dined;

不必为禁食推却，也可以忘记读书：
但是从他们的教堂看到弟兄被逐出，
他咆哮着讲真理，发天堂的语声，
使罪咎导向撒旦坠落路径的心寒战兢，
使脚步被吸引回转，死亡的耳能听。
他喊着："让愚昧人饥饿，我却谨慎
在我的巢中舒适生活，也必舒适而终。"

在那里站着无信仰者的现代品类，
被咒诅的栽子为地狱的种族。
他不像理神派，也不属基督徒，
一切原则，和一切品德，他一应俱无。
对于他，所有都是一样，不分善和恶，
耶和华，朱庇特，喇嘛，或是鬼魔；
穆罕默德的喊叫，或以赛亚的唱诗；
印地安人的祝禳，或基督徒的颂歌。
对于他，所有自然的意欲都是好的，
他嗜欲炖肉，或摩和克人嗜欲流血，
生成不能知道，或爱，全然美好的思想，
也摸不着路径飞翔到荣美的天堂。
但他最亲爱的自己选择大衰！去景仰；
去穿戴，去嬉戏，去赌咒，去酗酒，去嫖娼；
他去赛马；或别人竞赛，作手法欺骗；
他起誓，最快乐荣光是观赏斗鸡场。
他的灵魂没有穿着神圣的属性，
只是美好钟表弹簧在伟大的机器，
运作起来比睿腾豪斯的设计完美，
身体；人的主要部分；人，他自己；
人，是杰出的畜生最高贵的形体，
不披鬃毛的猪，没有尾巴的大猴子。
他光荣的目的：交配，吃喝，和死，
作牡蛎的坟场，肥嫩阉鸡的墓地。

48

Nor shrunk with fasting, nor with study pined:
Yet from their churches saw his brethren driven
Who thundered truth and spoke the voice of heaven,
Chilled trembling guilt, in Satan's headlong path
Charmed the feet back, and roused the ear of death.
"Let fools", he cried, "starve on, while prudent I
Snug in my nest shall live, and snug shall die."

There stood the infidel of modern breed,
Blest vegetation of infernal seed.
Alike no Deist, and no Christian, he;
But from all principle, all virtue, free.
To him all things the same, as good or evil:
Jehovah, Jove, the Lama, or the Devil;
Mohammed's braying, or Isaiah's lays;
The Indian's pow-wows; or the Christian's praise.
With him all natural desires are good:
His thrist for stews; the Mohawk's thirst for blood,
Made not to know, or love, the all-beauteous mind
Or wing through heaven his path to bliss refined.
But his dear self, choice Dagon! to adore;
To dress, to game, to swear, to drink, to whore;
To race his steeds; or cheat, when others run;
Pit tortured cocks, and swear 'tis glorious fun.
His soul not clothed with attributes divine
But a nice watch-spring to that grand machine,
That work more nice than Rittenhouse can plan;
The body; man's chief part; himself, the man;
Man, that illustrious brute of noblest shape,
A swine unbristled, and an untailed ape.
To couple, eat, and die- his glorious doom:
The oyster's churchyard, and the capon's tomb.

老之将至

克莱比 George Crabbe

六年又已过去，前面已过四十年纪，
时间开始玩它弄人的老把戏：
曾经在童女眼中俊美的鬓发，
从全褐的双鬓，出现入侵的银丝；
一度激情的热血，现在开始冷了，
时间强大的压力把人压低。
我像往常一样骑马或步行，
但现在不再有跃动的心灵；
现在中庸的速度就使我身体发暖，
中庸的距离就感觉双脚疲软。
我指给外地的客人壮丽的群山，
却说："不必去攀登，景色平凡。"
在朋友的大厦我开始畏怯
那冷然有序的客厅和华丽的陈设。
在家感觉比较安定的境况，
所有的东西要照我的规矩存放。
我停止去打猎；对我的马不再满意，
我更多爱宴席；我学习着棋。
我带着狗和枪出去，却不免叫狗失望，
因为我始终未发一枪。
我早晨的散步现在有时可缺，
称颂那恩雨叫我不必抉择。
实际上，我感觉懒散沉闷暗暗袭来，
善动的膀臂和矫捷的脚一去不再；
每天的琐细活动变成习惯，
新有的厌恶形式和时髦新鲜。
我爱的树木只是为了丢掉；
我数算着桃子，眼看收藏如何增高；
常说着同有故事，简单说，成为老套。

Six years had passed, and forty ere the six,

When Time began to play his usual tricks:

The locks once comely in a virgin's sight,

Locks of pure brown, displayed the encroaching white;

The blood, once fervid, now to cool began,

And Time's strong pressure to subdue the man.

I rode or walked as I was wont before,

But now the bounding spirit was no more;

A moderate pace would now my body heat,

A walk of moderate length distress my feet.

I showed my stranger guest those hills sublime,

But said, "The view is poor, we need not climb."

At a friend's mansion I began to dread

The cold neat parlor and the gay glazed bed;

At home I felt a more decided taste,

And must have all things in my order placed.

I ceased to hunt; my horses pleased me less,

My dinner more; I learned to play at chess.

I took my dog and gun, but saw the brute

Was disappointed that I did not shoot.

My morning walks I now could bear to lose,

And blessed the shower that gave me not to choose.

In fact, I felt a languor stealing on;

The active arm, the agile hand, were gone;

Small daily actions into habits grew,

And new dislike to forms and fashions new.

I loved my trees in order to dispose;

I numbered peaches, looked how stocks arose;

Told the same story oft, – in short, began to prose.

人之欲

昆瑞·亚当斯 John Quincy Adams

人在世上所需要的本来微少，
而且那微少的也不久长。
但在我的经验不尽如此；
虽然歌曲唱的是那样。
说起来我的需要颇多，
数下去哪怕没有百般；
虽则每个愿望都是巨金，
我仍然希望多多益善。

首先我要日用的饮食，
野味之外还要有酒。
当用膳时在我的桌上，
罗列着世间各地所有珍馐。
仅四道菜肴自然还不够，
略为满足我的食欲；
要有四名特选的法国名厨，
调制我的餐式适口悦目。

我还要，用王公的高价，
打扮得衣饰入时鲜丽豪华：
黑貂轻裘御寒冬的霜雪，
炎夏时则用丝罗绸纱，
克什米肩帔和布鲁塞尔花边，
从胸前直到外面装饰，
手上戴光耀的金钢钻，
颈项挂的是红宝石。

"Man wants but little here below,

Nor wants that little long."

'T is not with me exactly so;

But ' t is so in the song.

My wants are many and, if told,

Would muster many a score;

And were each wish a mint of gold,

I still should long for more.

What first I want is daily bread –

And canvas–backs – and wine –

And all the realms of nature spread

Before me, when I dine.

Four courses scarely can provide

My appetite to quell;

With four choice cooks from France beside,

To dress my dinner well.

What next I want, at princely cost,

Is elegant attire:

Black sable furs for winter' s frost,

And silks for summer' s fire,

And Cashmere shawls, and Brussels lace

My bosom' s front to deck, –

And diamond rings my hands to grace,

And rubies for my neck.

我还要(谁不想要?)一个妻子,
多情而又美丽;
能够安慰生活中一切的忧患,
也分享所有的欢喜。
她的脾气柔和,又能顺从,
情绪稳定而且恬静,
接纳我一切缺欠,依然爱我,
娴雅而有不变的深情。

随着时间的车不停地驶过,
我的财富积聚增加满仓盈屋,
我要多生男而且养女,
至少要八个或十全十足。
我要(呦!世人竟然敢
祈求如此的福分圆满?)
女孩子个个是贞洁的美娟,
男孩子都是智勇双全。

我要有热诚而忠实的朋友,
在逆境中能给我欢愉快慰;
他们永不会逢迎阿谀,
他们的膝也不会屈服于权威;
犯了错误时有朋友能谏诤责备,
在灵魂的深处我可以看得见;
我的友情也经得起考验,
显明对他人也同样的贞坚。

I want (who does not want?) a wife, –
Affectionate and fair;
To solace all the woes of life,
And all its joys to share.
Of temper sweet, of yielding will,
Of firm, yet placid mind, –
With all my faults to love me still
With sentiment refined.

And as Time' s car incessant runs,
And Fortune fills my store,
I want of daughters and of sons
From eight to half a score.
I want (alas! can mortal dare
Such bliss on earth to crave?)
That all the girls be chaste and fair, –
The boys all wise and brave.

I want a warm and faithful friend,
To cheer the adverse hour;
Who ne' er to flatter will descend,
Nor bend the knee to power–
A friend to chide me when I' m wrong,
My inmost soul to see;
And that my friendship prove as strong
For him as his for me.

我要有权力和高位的印记，
发号施令的徽旗；
受命于人民无私的恩典，
统治我祖国的土地；
我不要皇冠也不求权杖，
只要出于全国共同的意志；
或昼，或夜，致力于大业，
务求使国家的福杯满溢。

我要真诚的称赞声音，
跟随在我的身后，
将来的日子会想念，
这全人类的朋友，
许多世代之后，继起的人，
他们要宣告欢腾，
同声歌唱响彻天庭，
称颂我的荣名。

这些都是必死之人的欲望，
我不能欲望其存得久长，
因为人生不过是窄如手掌，
属地的福乐: 只是歌曲。
我末了的大欲, 结语:
当我归于泥土，
最后被呼唤见主，
我神的怜恤。

I want the seals of power and place,

The ensigns of command;

Charged by the People' s unbought grace

To rule my native land

Nor crown nor scepter would I ask

But from my country' s will,

By day, by night, to ply the task

Her cup of bliss to fill.

I want the voice of honest praise

To follow me behind,

And to be thought in future days

The friend of human kind,

That after ages, as they rise,

Exulting may proclaim

In choral union to the skies

Their blessings on my name.

These are the Wants of mortal Man –

I cannot want them long,

For life itself is but a span,

And earthly bliss—a song.

My last great Want – absorbing all –

Is, when beneath the sod,

And summoned to my final call,

The Mercy of My God.

神的仆人，作得成功

孟歌马利 James Montgomery

"神的仆人，作得成功；
　　息了你所爱的工；
胜利已得到，战争已打过，
　　进来同享你主人的欢乐。"
呼声临到时在夜半，
　　他上升去就听见，
死亡的箭穿过他的躯壳，
　　他倒下去,却全无惧怯。
在惊惶中能够安详，
　　当他身在疆场，
久年的战士和甲睡眠，
　　在他红十字架的盾牌下面：
仍有余温留在他手中的剑，
　　是因他新近的奋战；
命令一下，即时可以前征，
　　冒着矢石冲锋。
时在夜半呼声来临，
　　"预备迎见你的神！"
他醒起,元帅已经注意看到；
　　信心坚定正在祷告，
他的灵魂，欢跃前赴，
　　冲破现住的泥土；
日出时，遗留在地上，
　　是他残破黝黑的营帐。
痛苦和死亡都成为往事，
　　劳苦和忧伤终止；
生命长久的战争终于完成，
　　他的灵魂进入和平。
基督的战士，圆满功成，
　　颂赞是你新的事奉；
在那无尽的永世，
　　同救主享受欢乐安息。

"Servant of God, well done;
  Rest from thy loved employ;
The battle fought, the victory won,
  Enter thy Master's joy."
The voice at midnight came;
  He started up to hear,
A mortal arrow pierced his frame:
  He fell,–but felt no fear.
Tranquil amidst alarms,
  It found him in the field,
A veteran slumbering on his arms,
  Beneath his red–cross shield:
His sword was in his hand,
  Still warm with recent fight;
Ready that moment, at command,
  Through rock and steel to smite.
At midnight came the cry,
    "To meet thy God prepare!"
He woke,–and caught his Captain's eye;
  Then, strong in faith and prayer,
His spirit, with a bound,
  Burst its encumbering clay;
His tent, at sunrise, on the ground,
  A darkened ruin lay.
The pains of death are past,
  Labour and sorrow cease;
And life's long warfare closed at last,
  His soul is found in peace.
Soldier of Christ! well done;
  Praise be thy new employ;
And while eternal ages run,
  Rest in thy Saviour's joy.

布鲁斯和蜘蛛

巴屯 Bernard Barton

为了苏格兰的自由和权利，
　布鲁斯曾经尽心致力，
连续五次在战场搏击，
　也一连五次失意败绩；
再一次的进战英军，
结果仍然不如意
　他的部众又再溃奔；
从战场退下来，筋疲力尽，
成了无家可归的孤单逃犯
　在一个棚下躲避栖身。

想要争取宝座的他
　竟然落到这凄凉的地方：
他没有华美的宝盖，
　有的仅是粗陋的屋梁；
草铺的条椅是他唯一的床，
但即使那是天鹅绒的卧榻
　他也难以进入梦乡！
从暗夜到清晨的曙光，
为苏格兰和她的王权
　他躺在那里难眠沉想。

东方升起了光明的太阳，
　微光照着那不堪的眠床，
照着那支持低矮屋顶
　粗陋不成样子的屋梁。
抬起忧思的眼睛上望，

60

For Scotland's and for freedom's right

The Bruce his part had played,

In five successive fields of fight

Been conquered and dismayed;

Once more against the English host

His band he led, and once more lost

The meed for which he fought;

And now from battle, faint and worn,

The homeless fugitive forlorn

A hut's lone shelter sought.

And cheerless was that resting–place

For him who claimed a throne:

His canopy, devoid of grace,

The rude, rough beams alone;

The heather couch his only bed, –

Yet well I ween had slumber fled

From couch of eider–down!

Through darksome night till dawn of day,

Absorbed in wakeful thought he lay

Of Scotland and her crown.

The sun rose brightly, and its gleam

Fell on that hapless bed,

And tinged with light each shapeless beam

Which roofed the lowly shed;

When, looking up with wistful eye,

布鲁斯看见一只蜘蛛，
　　试图用柔细的丝结网
从小屋的梁往那梁上荡；
那昆虫尽力地奔忙
　　启导着苏格兰未来的王。

那思虑周详的蜘蛛
　　一连六次投出纤细的丝，
那细线飞荡乏力
　　或是迷失目标不济，
六次都失败了，却不放弃，
那忍耐的昆虫继续坚持，
　　绝不能动摇它的意志；
不久，当布鲁斯急切地注视，
看到它准备再一次的尝试，
　　尽它的勇气，力量，和战技。

再努力，第七次，最后一次！
　　那英雄赞扬它的表现！
在它所想望的梁上，
　　系紧了那蛛丝的细线；
虽然是微弱，却激起他的灵感，
使他思想，不仅仅是吉兆，
　　这功课实在是恰好，
明显不过任谁都能读得到：
坚毅者终必获得酬报，
　　忍耐赢得了赛跑。

The Bruce beheld a spider try

His filmy thread to fling

From beam to beam of that rude cot;

And well the insect's toilsome lot

Taught Scotland's future king.

Six times his gossamery thread

The wary spider threw;

In vain the filmy line was sped,

For powerless or untrue

Each aim appeared, and back recoiled

The patient insect, six times foiled,

And yet unconquered still;

And soon the Bruce, with eager eye,

Saw him prepare once more to try

His courage, strength, and skill.

One effort more, his seventh and last!

The hero hailed the sign!

And on the wished–for beam hung fast

That slender, silken line;

Slight as it was, his spirit caught

The more than omen, for his thought

The lesson well could trace,

Which even "he who runs may read,"

That Perseverance gains its meed,

And Patience wins the race.

西拿基立的毁灭

拜伦
Lord George Gordon Byron

亚述人下来如同狼入羊圈，
他的军队穿戴着金紫闪现；
枪矛的光耀像星在海面上，
加利利夜海翻腾蓝色波浪。

如同夏天林间丰绿的树叶，
落日照着大军飘扬的旗帜；
如同秋风吹过林间的枯叶，
明晨大军的旗帜散落堆积。

死亡的天使展开他的翅膀，
经过时吹气在仇敌的脸上；
睡者的眼都变成定着冷僵，
他们的心也停息不再激扬。

那里躺卧的战马鼻孔全张，
只是没有喷出气息的骄狂；
奔跑的白色口沫凝在草上，
像是冲击岩石散落的碎浪。

那里躺卧着骑士苍白扭曲，
战甲上有褐锈眉间有冷露：
帐幕静寂无声旌旗不飞舞，
号角不再吹响戈矛无人举。

亚述的寡妇举起哀声遍地，
巴力庙里的偶像也都破碎；
外邦的军威不是刀剑击溃，
神只一观看就如雪融冰颓。

The Assyrian came down like the wolf on the fold,

And his cohorts were gleaming in purple and gold;

And the sheen of their spears was like stars on the sea,

When the blue wave rolls nightly on deep Galilee.

Like the leaves of the forest when summer is green,

That host with their banners at sunset were seen:

Like the leaves of the forest when autumn hath blown,

That host on the morrow lay withered and strown.

For the Angel of Death spread his wings on the blast,

And breathed in the face of the foe as he passed;

And the eyes of the sleepers waxed deadly and chill,

And their hearts but once heaved– and for ever stood still!

And there lay the steed with his nostril all wide,

But through it there rolled not the breath of his pride;

And the foam of his gasping lay white on the turf,

And cold as the spray of the rock–beating surf.

And there lay the rider distorted and pale,

With the dew on his brow, and the rust on his mail:

And the tents were all silent– the banners alone–

The lances unlifted– the trumpet unblown.

And the widows of Ashur are loud in their wail,

And the idols are broke in the temple of Baal;

And the might of the Gentile, unsmote by the sword,

Hath melted like snow in the glance of the Lord!

在巴比伦河边

拜伦 *Lord George Gordon Byron*

我们坐下哀哭在巴别水边，
　追想过去的那一天，
撒冷的高处作仇敌的猎物，
　他们在任意杀戮叫喊，
你们，她不幸的女儿！
　全都哭泣着远离被赶散。

当我们悲哀地向河水注视
　在脚下自由的奔流不息，
他们命令我们唱一只歌，
　但，噢，永不屈服让外人胜利！
宁愿这右手永远枯干，
　也不会奏竖琴娱乐仇敌！

把我们的竖琴悬挂上垂柳，
　噢，撒冷！它听来该是自由；
当你荣耀终止的时候，
　那表征仍在我心存留：
当房掠者的声音在我身旁，
　我永不调和柔美的韵奏！

We sat down and wept by the waters

    Of Babel, and thought of the day

When our foe, in the hue of his slaughters,

    Made Salem's high places his prey;

And Ye, oh her desolate daughters!

    Were scattered all weeping away.

While sadly we gazed on the river

    Which rolled on in freedom below,

They demanded the song; but, oh never

    That triumph the Stranger shall know!

May this right hand be withered for ever,

    Ere it string our high harp for the foe!

On the willow that harp is suspended,

    Oh Salem! its sound should be free;

And the hour when thy glories were ended

    But let me that token of thee:

And ne'er shall its soft tones be blended

    With the voice of the Spoiler by me!

敖兹曼帝亚

雪莱 Percy B. Shelly

我遇到一个旅人来自古老的土地，

他说：有两条巨大没有躯干的腿石

矗立在沙漠中……附近的沙里，

半沉埋着一个残破的面容，蹙着额，

努着唇，冷酷的命令鄙夷；

显示着雕像者熟知这些神情

依然存留，印在没有生命的物体上，

那制造者的手，心理感受是这样；

座台上的铭文如此刻着：

　　我的名字是敖兹曼帝亚，诸王之王，

　　看看我的功业，大能者，你休想！

此外别无所有。旁边那朽败

的伟大残骸，无边而荒凉，

寂寞的平沙伸展向远方。

*敖兹曼帝亚是埃及王法老兰塞二世(Ramses II)的希腊文名字，可能就是摩西奉神差遣领以色列

人出埃及时的统治者。

I met a traveller from an antique land,

Who said: "Two vast and trunkless legs of stone

Stand in the desert. Near them on the sand,

Half sunk, a shattered visage lies, whose frown,

And wrinkled lip and sneer of cold command,

Tell that its sculptor well those passions read

Which yet survive, stamped on these lifeless things,

The hand that mocked them and the heart that fed;

And on the pedestal these words appear:

   'My name is Ozymandias, King of Kings,

Look on my Works, ye Mighty, and despair!'

Nothing beside remains. Round the decay

Of the colossal wreck, boundless and bare

The lone and level sands stretch far away."

清教徒移民登陆

菲莉雪·海门斯 Felicia D. Hemans

苍凉多石的海岸上，
激溅着飞扬的碎浪，
阴沉风暴的天空下，
树木巨大的枝柯在摇荡；

黑沉沉的夜暗低悬，
覆盖着山头和水边，
负载着流浪者的小船，
碇泊在新英格兰荒凉的海岸。

不是要作征服者，
他们带着真诚的心；
不曾打着激扬的战鼓，
也没有号角吹起声威远闻；

他们不是逃亡飘泊，
心怀着惧怕畏怯静默；
他们用欢乐昂扬的诗歌，
震撼着沉郁的荒漠。

在风浪中他们歌唱，
超越了海涛达到了群星；
幽暗的林径也发出回响，
应和着自由的歌声。

The breaking waves dashed high

On a stern and rock—bound coast,

And the woods against a stormy sky

Their giant branches tossed;

And the heavy night hung dark

The hills and waters o' er,

When a band of exiles moored their bark

On the wild New England shore.

Not as the conqueror comes,

They, the true—hearted came;

Nor with the roll of the stirring drums,

And the trumpet that sings of fame;

Not as the flying come,

In silence and in fear –

They shook the depths of the desert gloom

With their hymns of loft cheer.

Amidst the storm they sang,

And the stars heard, and the sea;

And the sounding aisles of the dim woods rang

To the anthem of the free.

雄鹰离巢凌空直上，
海洋绽开白色的浪花；
树林摇舞松风呼啸，
是在欢迎他们到家。

在那群移民者当中，
有些人已经是鬓发斑白；
是什么使他们离开童年的故土，
到这遥远的异乡来？

那里一位妇女无畏的眼睛，
闪耀着对真理的深爱；
那里有男子高贵的眉宇间，
显示青年燃烧的壮怀。

他们何所寻求来自远方？
是为闪耀珍宝的矿藏？
是海上的丰富或战争的掠物报赏？
他们是寻求纯洁信仰的殿堂。

是的，他们的脚刚一登陆，
就称这里为圣地；
他们不愿被沾染，而现在
寻得了敬拜上主的自由。

*1620 年 11 月 20 日，首批英国清教徒移民搭乘"五月花号"(Mayflower)抵达美洲东海岸；称这
地方为 Plymouth，在今马萨诸塞州。以后，为了纪念先民登陆，定为感恩节。

The ocean eagle soared

　　From his nest by the white wave' s foam;

And the rocking pines of the forest roared–

　　This was their welcome home.

There were men with hoary hair

　　Amidst that pilgrim band:

Why had they come to wither there,

　　Away from their childhood' s land.

There was a woman' s fearless eye,

　　Lit by her deep love' s truth;

There was manhood' s brow serenely high,

　　And the fiery heart of youth.

What sought they thus afar?

　　Bright jewels of the mine?

The wealth of seas, the spoils of war?

　　They sought a faith' s pure shrine!

Aye, call it holy ground,

　　The soil where they first trod;

They have left unstained what there they found –

　　Freedom to worship God.

从深沉的幽暗中

济慈 John Keats

像深沉的幽暗中一只银色的鸽子

    冲上去，射入东方的光明，

扇动的双翼上负载着欢乐满盈，

你的灵魂也是这样飞入天庭，

那里是永远的爱与和平；

在那里，快乐的灵魂戴着冠冕，嵌镶

着星的光芒，荣耀辉煌，

享至高的喜乐只有蒙福的人得尝。

你或参加那不朽的诗班歌唱，

用天上荣美的旋律

充满至高的赐福，或随

全能天父的意欲，穿越天空

传送神的圣谕，喜乐无可言喻，

为何让忧伤损害我们的欢愉？

As from the darkening gloom a silver dove

Upsoars, and darts into the Eastern light,

On pinions that naught moves but pure delight,

So fled thy soul into the realms above,

Regions of peace and everlasting love;

Where happy spirits, crown'd with circlets bright

Of starry beam, and gloriously bedight,**

Taste the high joy none but the blest can prove.

There thou or joinest the immortal quire

In melodies that even Heaven fair

Fill with superior bliss, or, at desire

Of the omnipotent Father, cleavest the air

On holy message sent—What pleasure's higher

Wherefore does any grief our joy impair?

贫民临终

珀斯
Caroline Bowles

轻步缓行，低下头，
　　恭敬肃静把头低下，
没有敲响丧钟，
但一个不朽的灵魂，
　　现在临终。

陌生人！不问你如何伟大，
　　谦卑恭敬把头低下；
有一位在那残破的棚
在那简陋的床上，
　　比你更伟大。

在乞丐的屋顶下，
　　看哪，死亡的仪式在进行。
进来，没有群众参加；
进来，没有侍卫护驾
　　这个王宫的大门。

地下阴冷潮湿，
　　没有微笑宫廷人士的足迹；
一个静默的女人站立，
枯瘦的双手举起
　　首领已经濒死。

Tread softly,– bow the head,–

In reverent silence bow,–

No passing bell doth toll,

Yet an immortal soul

Is passing now.

Stranger! however great,

With lowly reverence bow;

There' s one in that poor shed –

One by that paltry bed –

Greater than thou.

Beneath that beggar' s roof,

Lo! Death doth keep his state.

Enter, no crowds attend;

Enter, no guards defend

This palace gate.

That pavement, damp and cold,

No smiling courtiers tread;

One silent woman stands,

Lifting with meagre hands

A dying head.q

没有混杂的声音，

   独有一个婴孩在哭喊；

低掩的饮泣哽咽，重现

深而短促的喘，最后

   临去的呻吟。

啊，改变！啊，奇异的改变！

   冲破监狱的栅栏，

此时在那里那么低贱，

那么悲惨，忽然

   超越星辰之间。

啊，改变！伟大的改变！

   那里躺卧着失去灵魂的躯壳；

太阳永远照耀，

新的不朽醒觉，

   醒起与他的神同在。

No mingling voices sound,–

    An infant wail alone;

A sob suppressed,– again

That short deep gasp, and then –

    The parting groan.

O change! O wondrous change!

    Burst are the prison bars,–

This moment there so low,

So agonized, and now

    Beyond the stars.

O change! stupendous change!

    There lies the soulless clod;

The sun eternal breaks,

The new immortal wakes,–

    Wakes with his God.

必死之人何必心高气傲？

威廉·诺克司 William Knox

噢，必死之人何必心高气傲？
像一颗飞驰的流星，一片快过的云雾，
一道闪电，一个碎浪的泡沫，
人从生命进入他安息的坟墓。
橡树和杨柳的叶子必要凋敝，
四散飘落又堆积在一起；
年轻的和年老的，卑贱和高贵，
都必腐朽化为尘土一抔。

母亲对她的婴孩爱护关怀，
婴孩向母亲报以情爱；
丈夫有母子是他的恩赐，
一个一个，全都要归宿安息。
那少女的面颊，眉梢，和眼睛，
闪耀着美貌和快乐，借以得胜；
那些对她爱慕和称赞的记忆，
俱都从活着的心头抹除消逝。

君王那曾握过权杖的手，
祭司那戴过圣冠的眉头，
智者的眼睛和勇者的心，
都沉埋在墓中无处可寻。
农夫本分是撒种和收割，
牧人领他的羊爬上陡坡，
乞丐为了讨饭到处流浪，
凋落像被践踏的草一样。

那曾享受与天堂团契的圣徒；
或顽强的罪人执迷不肯悔悟；
义人和罪咎者，智慧和劣愚，
都默然地埋骨混杂着尘土。

这是林肯总统 (Abraham Lincoln, 1809—1865) 从早年就特别喜爱的一首诗。他剪存报纸，遍访其诗作者不得。

80

O, why should the spirit of mortal be proud?
Like a swift–fleeting meteor, a fast–flying cloud,
A flash of the lightning, a break of the wave,
Man passes from life to his rest in the grave.
The leaves of the oak and the willow shall fade,
Be scattered around and together be laid;
And the young and the old, and the low and the high,
Shall moulder to dust and together shall lie.

The infant a mother attended and loved,
The mother that infant' s affection who proved;
The husband that mother and infant who blessed,
Each, all, are away to their dwellings of rest.
The maid on whose cheek, on whose brow, in whose eye,
Shone beauty and pleasure,– her triumphs are by;
And the memory of those who loved her and praised,
Are alike from the minds of living erased.

The hand of the king that the sceptre hath borne;
The brow of the priest that the mitre hath worn;
The eye of the sage and the heart of the brave,
Are hidden and lost in the depth of the grave.
The peasant, whose lot was to sow and to reap;
The herdsman, who climbed with his goats up the steep;
The beggar, who wandered in search of his bread,
Have faded away like the grass that we tread.

The saint who enjoyed the communion of heaven,
The sinner who dared to remain unforgiven,
The wise and the foolish, the guilty and just,
Have quietly mingled their bones in the dust.

这样，群众都像花或杂草消失，
凋谢枯干让另一代继起代替；
这样，群众来过，当我们注视，
重复再絮说那些已常听的故事。

我们仍然像先人的故我旧样：
我们看的是先人看过的景象，
我们饮于同一泉源看同一太阳，
也同先人跑在那同一路径上。
我们的心意想先人同样的思想：
我们逃避死亡像先人逃避死亡，
我们想延长生命先人也想延长，
但生命如飞而去像鸟展开翅膀。

他们爱过，那些艳事已难以再讲；
他们轻蔑，那骄傲的心已经冰凉；
他们悲伤，长眠者没有哀哭声响；
他们欢乐，舌头无声喜信难传扬。
他们死去，唉！死了：我们现在存留，
我们走在他们躺卧的墓地上头，
这里只是他们暂时的寄身之处，
要遇到那些在朝圣旅途所曾相遇的。

是啊！希望和失望，痛苦和喜乐，
在晴天和阴雨中我们交互会合；
有欢笑和眼泪，有哀曲和乐歌，
仍然要互相伴随，一波又一波。
只是转瞬之间，只是呼吸的一息，
从盛壮的健康就到苍白的死，
从镀金的厅堂到棺架和尸衣，
噢，必死的人何必心高气傲？

So the multitude goes, like the flowers or the weed
That withers away to let others succeed;
So the multitude comes, even those we behold,
To repeat every tale that has often been told.

For we are the same our fathers have been;
We see the same sights our fathers have seen,–
We drink the same stream and view the same sun,
And run the same course our fathers have run.
The thoughts we are thinking our fathers would think;
From the death we are shrinking our fathers would shrink,
To the life we are clinging they also would cling;
But it speeds for us all, like a bird on the wing.

They loved, but the story we cannot unfold;
They scorned, but the heart of the haughty is cold;
They grieved, but no wail from their slumbers will come;
They joyed, but the tongue of their gladness is dumb.
They died, ay! they died: and we things that are now,
Who walk on the turf that lies over their brow,
Who make in their dwelling a transient abode,
Meet the things that they met on their pilgrimage road.

Yea! hope and despondency, pleasure and pain,
We mingle together in sunshine and rain;
And the smiles and the tears, the song and the dirge,
Still follow each other, like surge upon surge.
'T is the wink of an eye, ' t is the draught of a breath,
From the blossom of health to the paleness of death,
From the gilded saloon to the bier and the shroud,–
O, why should the spirit of mortal be proud?

伐木者，留下那树

莫锐斯 George P. Morris

伐木者，留下那树！
　不要伤它一根树枝！
在幼年时它曾荫庇我，
　现在我要对它护庇。
是我先祖的手，
　栽植在他的村舍旁，
伐木者，让它立在原处，
　不要动斧将它损伤！
那棵熟识的树，
　它的名声和荣耀，
传扬到陆地和海岛，
　你怎好把它砍倒！
伐木者，手下留情！
　莫把它连地的根斩断，
噢，留下那棵老橡树，
　现在已经巍然顶天！

当还只是个嬉戏的顽童，
　我常来到它可爱的荫下；
任所有的欢乐迸发，
　我妹妹也来这里玩耍。
妈妈在这里亲吻我，
　爸爸捏着我的手
请原谅这些痴情的眼泪，
　只让这棵老橡树存留。
我的心丝萦绕着你，
　贴近如你的树皮，老朋友！
你的树枝仍然要伸展，
　野鸟要歌唱在枝头，
老树啊，你还要忍受风暴！
　伐木者，请你走开；
当我还有手能拯救，
　斧头就不可加害。

Woodman, spare that tree!
Touch not a single bough!
In youth it sheltered me,
And I'll protect it now.
'T was my forefather's hand
That placed it near his cot;
There, woodman, let it stand,
The axe shall harm it not!
That old familiar tree,
Whose glory and renown
Are spread o'er land and sea,
And wouldst thou hew it down!
Woodman, forbear thy stroke!
Cut not its earth-bound ties;
O, spare that aged oak,
Now towering to the skies!

When but an idle boy
I sought its grateful shade;
In all their gushing joy
Here too my sisters played.
My mother kissed me here;
My father pressed my hand –
Forgive this foolish tear,
But let that old oak stand.
My heart-strings round thee cling,
Close as thy bark, old friend!
Here shall the wild-bird sing,
And still thy branches bend,
Old tree! the storm still brave!
And, woodman, leave the spot;
While I've a hand to save,
Thy axe shall hurt it not.

母亲的圣经

莫锐斯 George P. Morris

现在，这书是唯一留下给我的，
　　眼泪不禁开始倾流，
用抖颤的嘴唇和震动的眉梢，
　　我把它紧压在我的心头。
这里是我们家谱系的树，
　　许多代都已度过；
我母亲的手握过的《圣经》，
　　她，临终把它给我。
啊！我清楚地记得
　　这些人的名字写在上面；
在晚上的祷告过后，
　　全家时常一同围在炉边，
谈论着那书叶所说的，
　　那语声使我的心激动！
现在他们都已静默死亡，
　　却仍然活在我这心中！

我父亲诵读这本圣书，
　　给亲爱的众姊妹和弟兄，
可怜的母亲看来那么宁静，
　　神的话她最爱听！
她天使般的面容我依然看见！
　　聚来的记忆何等生动！
在家的厅堂里面，
　　那个小组再次相逢！
你是最可靠相知的朋友，
　　我体验过你不变的坚贞；
是我的顾问和向导，
　　所有的人虚假，唯你真诚。
任用地上所有的矿藏财宝来买，
　　都不能同这书卷相比；
它教导我生活的道路，
　　先教导我如何死！

86

This book is all that's left me now, –
    Tears will unbidden start, –
With faltering lip and throbbing brow
    I press it to my heart.
For many generations past
    Here is our family tree;
My mother's hands this Bible clasped,
    She, dying, gave it me.
Ah! well do I remember those
    Whose names these records bear;
Who round the hearthstone used to close,
    After the evening prayer,
And speak of what these pages said
    In tones my heart would thrill!
Though they are with the silent dead,
    Here are they living still!

My father read this holy book
    To brothers, sisters, dear;
How calm was my poor mother's look,
    Who loved God's word to hear!
Her angel face, – I see it yet!
    What thronging memories come!
Again that little group is met
    Within the halls of home!
Thou truest friend man ever knew,
    Thy constancy I've tried;
When all were false, I found thee true,
    My counsellor and guide.
The mines of earth no treasures give
    That could this volume buy;
In teaching me the way to live,
    It taught me how to die!

My Mother's Bible

我们感谢你

爱默生 Ralph Waldo Emerson

为花朵绕着我们的脚步开放；
为柔软的草，那样清新芳香；
为蜜蜂的嗡叫和群鸟的歌唱；
为美好的万有我们听和观赏；
天上的父啊，我们感谢你！

为蓝的水流，为蔚蓝的天空；
为可爱的绿荫树枝高向苍穹；
为芬芳的空气和清凉的微风；
为树丛发出幽美悠长的啸鸣；
天上的父啊，我们感谢你！

为母亲的慈爱，父亲护卫关照；
为弟兄们强壮，姊妹秀丽美貌；
为家庭的爱和每天去上学校；
为你的引导免我们偏离正道；
天上的父啊，我们感谢你！

为了你慈爱，永远的臂膀，
支持我们越过所有祸患损伤；
为神圣赐福的话语长久以往，
现在帮助我们对你旨意明朗；
天上的父啊，我们感谢你！

For flowers that bloom about our feet;

For tender grass, so fresh and sweet;

For song of bird and hum of bee;

For all things fair we hear or see

Father in heaven, we thank thee!

For blue of stream, for blue of sky;

For pleasant shade of branches high;

For fragant air and cooling breeze;

For beauty of the blowing trees—

Father in heaven, we thank thee!

For mother—love, for father—care;

For brothers strong and sisters fair;

For love at home and school each day;

For guidance lest we go astray—

Father in heaven, we thank thee!

For Thy dear, everlasting arms,

That bear us o' er all ills and harms;

For blessed words of long ago,

That help us now Thy will to know—

Father in heaven, we thank thee!

西西里王罗波

朗菲罗 Henry Wadsworth Longfellow

西西里王罗波，是教皇乌尔班的弟弟，
阿勒冥的皇帝华蒙是他的长兄，
身穿华贵的衣饰，
带着大群的武士和侍从，
在圣约翰节日晚祷时，傲然坐着
听教牧吟唱"尊主颂"。
当他听着，一遍又一遍的
重复，仿佛是抑制和担重，
当听到了："他叫有权柄的
失位，叫卑贱的高升"；
他慢慢抬起王者尊贵的头，
垂询身边识字的秘书随从：
"这句话是什么意思？"秘书立即回应：
"他使有权能的从高位降卑，
高举没有地位的上腾。"

罗波王鄙夷地低声说：
"好在这种煽动性的语句
只由教职人员用拉丁语唱诵；
让教牧们和人民都知道，
没有什么能力推翻我的宝座权柄！"
靠在椅背上，他打个呵欠，入睡了，
单调的唱诵使他睡意更浓。
当他醒转时，已经是夜间，
空荡荡的教堂，全然没有光亮，
只有几盏残灯，发着微弱的火焰，
照出淡淡的黄晕在圣徒的像旁。
他从座位上四围环望，
看不见什么活物，也听不到声响。
他摸索到门前，但门已经锁上，
他大声喊叫，听着，再又敲撞，

Robert of Sicily, brother of Pope Urbane

And Valmond, Emperor of Allemaine,

Apparelled in magificent attire,

With retinue of many a knight and squire,

On St. John' s eve, at vespers, proudly sat

And heard the priests chant the Magnificat.

And as he listened, o' er and o' er again

Repeated, like a burden or refrain,

He caught the words, "Deposuit potentes

De sede, et exaltavit humiles;"

And slowly lifting up his kingly head

He to a learned clerk beside him said,

   "What mean these words?" The clerk made answer meet,

   "He has put down the mighty from their seat,

And has exalted them of low degree.

Thereat King Robert muttered scornfully,

   "Tis well that such seditious words are sung

Only by priests and in the Latin tongue;

For unto priests and people be it known,

There is no power can push me from my throne!"

And leaning back, he yawned and fell asleep,

Lulled by the chant monotonous and deep.

When he awoke, it was already night;

The church was empty, and there was no light,

Save where the lamps, that glimmered few and faint,

Lighted a little space before some saint.

He started from his seat and gazed around,

But saw no living thing and heard no sound.

He groped towards the door, but it was locked;

He cried aloud, and listened, and then knocked,

发着可怕的恫吓，加上抱怨，
他咒诅人，也祈求圣徒帮忙。
如同死去的圣像在那里嘲笑，
空有回响来自屋顶和墙。

最后，管教堂的从外面听见
那喊叫的扰攘和敲门，
以为是盗贼进入了祷告的殿，
挑着灯笼来查问："是什么人？"
半气结的罗波王盛怒回答：
"是我，王！你害怕吗？给我开门！"
管堂的受了惊，自言自语，诅咒着说：
"是酒醉的流浪汉，或更下等的恶棍！"
用那把大钥匙猛然把教堂门敞开，
一条大汉跨大步冲到了他身旁，
凶悍的，没有帽子或外衣，赤着臂膀，
并没有转身，不睬他，半句话不讲，
但跳进了漆黑的夜暗里，
失去了踪影像幽灵一样。

西西里王罗波，教皇乌尔班的弟弟，
他的长兄是阿勒冥的华蒙皇帝，
被剥去了华贵的衣饰，
光着头，喘吁吁的，满身污泥，
暴怒如雷大踏步到了宫门，
感受侮辱，怒气填胸却无法可施，
冲过了庭院，找人发泄，
左右的僮仆和管家执事，
在火把下照着他苍白的面孔，
急忙跑上宽阔和回音的楼梯。
他匆促地穿堂复过室，

And uttered awful threatenings and complaints,
And imprecations upon men and saints.
The sounds reechoed from the roof and walls
As if dead priests were laughing in their stalls.

At length the sexton, hearing from without
The tumult of the knocking and the shout,
And thinking thieves were in the house of prayer,
Came with his lantern, asking, "Who is there?"
Half choked with rage, King Robert fiercely said:
  "Open: ' t is I, the King! Art thou afraid?"
The frightened sexton, muttering, with a curse,
  "This is some drunken vagabond, or worse!"
Turned the great key and flung the portal wide;
And man rushed by him at a single stride,
Haggard, half naked, without hat or cloak,
Who neither turned, nor looked at him, nor spoke,
But leaped into the blackness of the night,
And vanished like a spectre from his sight.

Robert of Sicily, brother of Pope Urbane
And Valmond, Emperor of Allemaine,
Despoiled of his magnificent attire,
Bareheaded, breathless, and besprent with mire,
With sense of wrong and outrage desperate,
Strode on and thundered at the palace gate;
Rushed through the courtyard, thrusting in his rage
To right and left each seneschal and page,
And hurried up the broad and sounding stair,
His white face ghastly in the torches' glare.
From hall to hall he passed with breathless speed;

他听到在喊叫发声，却无人置理，
最后到达了宴会厅，
灯烛辉煌，扑鼻的熏香气息。

厅堂一端高坐着另一位王，
戴着他御印的戒指，他的王冠和衣裳，
是罗波王的身材，同样相貌和形状，
只是全部变化成天使的荣光！
那是一个天使；他在那里
到处充满了他神圣的辉煌，
高贵的气质透过他的形体，
只是没有谁能认出是天使的化装。

那失去宝座的王向天使注视，
一时惊讶无言，不能够行动，
遇到他的忿怒和惊奇，
目光中带着神圣的怜悯神情；
他说："你是谁，竟敢到这里来？"
换来的是罗波王回答讥讽：
"我是王，要来收复
被你这假冒者篡夺的朝廷！"
这大胆无礼的话，忽然
使座上客人都跳起来，纷纷拔剑反应；
那天使连眉头也不皱平静地说：
"不，不是王，是王的小丑一名，
今后要戴上海扇帽，佩着铜铃，
带一只猿猴作你的参谋随从；
你要顺服王的仆役使唤，
服侍我的侍从们在堂前听命！"

无人管他的恫吓喊叫和祈求，

Voices and cries he heard, but did not heed,
Until at last he reached the banquet–room,
Blazed with light, and breathing with perfume.

There on the dais sat another king,
Wearing his robes, his crown, his signet–ring,
King Robert's self in features, form, and height,
But all transfigured with angelic light!
It was an Angel; and his presence there
With a divine effulgence filled the air,
An exaltation, piercing the disguise,
Though none the hidden Angel recognize.

A moment speechless, motionless, amazed,
The throneless monarch on the Angel gazed,
Who met his look of anger and surprise
With the divine compassion of his eyes;
Then said, "Who art thou? and why com'st thou here?"
To which King Robert answered with a sneer,
"I am the King, and come to claim my own
From an impostor, who usurps my throne!"
And suddenly, at these audacious words,
Up sprang the angry guests, and drew their swords;
The Angel answered, with unruffled brow,
"Nay, not the King, but the King's Jester, thou
Henceforth shalt wear the bells and scalloped cape,
And for thy counsellor shalt lead an ape;
Thou shalt obey my sevants when they call,
And wait upon my benchmen in the hall!"

Deaf to King Robert's threats and cries and prayers,

他们把他推下楼梯赶出厅堂；
一群僮仆们窃笑着在前面跑，
当他们把摺门开敞，
听到了武士们在哄然狂笑，
他的心下沉了，有奇异的紧张，
高大的房顶哄起回响，
嘲弄的恭贺说："万岁我王！"

次日清早，第一线曙光使他复醒，
他自己心里说："那不过是个梦！"
当他转头的时候身下的稻草窸窣有声，
旁边是他的小丑帽子和铜铃，
周围是没有装饰褪色的墙壁，
不远处是群驹在嚼草的马棚，
在角落里，有个活动的身影，
是那可怜的猿猴在瑟缩着叽喳做声。
那不是梦，他所深爱的世界
已经变作了尘灰，着手成空！

一天天过去又复再来，
西西里恢复了上古盛世；
在天使的统治善政之下，
那快乐的海岛五谷登丰新酒洋溢，
在火山灼热的胸膛之下，
那古老的巨人也恬然安息。
这样，罗波王也自己安分由命，
不得安慰，阴郁的沉闷安静。
穿着小丑的杂色花衣，
看来似是迷失，直直无神的眼睛，
从下巴到耳朵上边刮得净光像僧，
忍受着侍从的讥讽僮仆的嘲弄，

They thrust him from the hall and down the stairs;
A group of tittering pages ran before,
And as they opened wide the folding–door,
His heart failed, for he heard, with strange alarms,
The boisterous laughter of the men–at–arms,
And all the vaulted chamber roar and ring
With the mock plaudits of "Long live the King!"

Next morning, waking with the day' s first beam,
He said within himself, "It was a dream!"
But the straw rustled as he turned his head,
There were the cap and bells beside his bed,
Around him rose the bare, discolored walls,
Close by, the steeds were champing in their stalls,
And in the corner, a revolting shape,
Shivering and chattering sat the wretched ape.
It was no dream; the world he loved so much
Had turned to dust and ashes at his touch!

Days came and went; and now returned again
To Sicily the old Saturnian reign;
Under the Angel' s governance benign
The happy island danced with corn and wine,
And deep within the mountain' s burning breast
Enceladus, the giant, was at rest.
Meanwhile King Robert yielded to his fate,
Sullen and silent and disconsolate.
Dressed in the motley garb that Jesters wear,
With look bewildered and a vacant stare,
Close shaven above the ears, as monks are shorn,
By courtiers mocked, by pages laughed to scorn,

他唯一的朋友是那只猿猴，他的食物
是别人吃过的残饭剩羹，他仍然不认输定。
当那天使偶然相遇在途中，
半认真的对他说话，有一半嘲讽，
严肃的，却是轻柔，他觉得似乎是
天鹅绒的鞘藏着青钢利刃的刀锋：
"你是王吗?"刺着他的隐痛
他会忽然迸发难以藏容；
昂起他的额头，粗率的说：
"我是，我是王!"傲岸回应。

大约三年过去了，来了，
特使尊贵又有盛名，
是阿勒冥皇帝华蒙差来转达，
教皇乌尔班向罗波王发出的邀请，
那信是要他立即启程，
在圣礼拜四到达他的罗马城。
那天使对来使盛大欢迎，
给他们礼物和锦绣外套，
天鹅绒披肩有华贵的勋衔
给他们戒指和稀世的珠宝。
然后同他们一道扬帆启航，
从海上到了可爱的意大利半岛；
显赫的行列引得万人瞩目，
大群的扈从还有马队前导，
鞍辔屉镫都是镶金嵌玉，
全都衣冠鲜明还插着彩色羽毛。
看，在仆人中间，有个可笑的角色
有一匹杂种跛马蹒跚而行，
罗波王骑着，外衣缀着狐狸尾飘动随风，
那猿猴端肃地在驾驭，一本正经，

His only friend the ape, his only food
What others left,—he still was unsubdued,
And when the Angel met him on his way,
And half in earnest, half in jest, would say,
Sternly, though tenderly, that he might feel
The velvet acabbard held a sword of steel,
   "Art thou the King?" the passion of his woe
Burst from him in resistless overflow,
And, lifting high his forehead, he would fling
The haughty answer back,   "I am, I am the King!"

Almost three years were ended; when there came
Ambassadors of great repute and name
From Valmond, Emperor of Allemiane,
Unto King Robert, saying that Pope Urbane
By letter summoned them forthwith to come
On Holy Thursday to his city of Rome.
The Angel with great joy received his guests,
And gave them presents of embroidered vests,
And velvet mantles with rich ermine lined,
And rings and jewels of the rarest kind.
Then he departed with them o' er the sea
Into the lovely land of Italy,
Whose loveliness was more resplendent made
By the mere passing of that cavalcade,
With plumes, and cloaks, and housings, and the stir
Of jewelled bridle and of golden spur.
And lo! among the menials, in mock state,
Upon a piebald steed, with shambling gait,
His cloak of fox—tails flapping in the wind,
The solemn ape demurely perched behind,

所经过全国的大小城镇，
总是有大批来取乐的观众。

教皇迎接他们以盛壮的声势，
圣彼得广场上，鸣号又悬挂旌旗。
为他们祝福又加上拥抱，
热烈的尽足使徒的恩赐和礼仪。
他既有颂贺复再祝祷，
不知不觉地接待了天使。
小丑罗波，忽然从人丛中冒了出来，
到他们的面前高声大嚷：
"我是王！看，认清我本人
罗波，你的亲兄弟，西西里王！
你眼前这个人，有我的形象，
是假冒的王，在装模作样。
你不认得我？心里岂没有声音
答应我的呼求，承认我是骨肉同堂？"
教皇静默不言，表现困惑心意摇荡，
看着天使的面貌是那么安详；
皇帝笑着说："真有他的奇风异想，
把一个狂人当小丑来豢养！"
可怜的小丑受尽奚落面目无光，
挤回到人丛里悄然躲藏。

庄严的受难周来而复往，
复活节主日清晨露出曙光，
天使的临在，带着荣美，
在日出以前把全城照亮，
新的热诚充满了人的心间，
觉得基督复活的真实无妄。
连那个小丑在他稻草的床，

King Robert rode, making huge merriment
In all the country towns through which they went.

The Pope received them with great pomp and blare
Of bannered trumpets, on Saint Peter's aquare,
Giving his benediction and embrace,
Fervent, and full of apostolic grace.
While with congratulations and with prayers
He entertained the Angel unaweres,
Robert, the Jester, bursting through the crowd,
Into their presence rushed, and cried aloud,
   "I am the King! Look, and behold in me
Robert, your brother, King of Sicily!
This man, who wears my semblance to your eyes,
Is an impostor in a king's disguise.
Do you not know me? does no voice within
Answer my cry, and say we are akin?"
The Pope in silence, but with troubled mien,
Gazed at the Angel's countenance serene;
The Emperor, laughing, said, "It is stange sport
To keep a madman for thy Fool at court!"
And the poor, baffled Jester in disgrace
Was hustled back among the populace.

In solemn state the Holy Week went by,
And Easter Sunday gleamed upon the sky;
The presence of the Angel, with its light,
Before the sun rose, made the city bright,
And with new fervor filled the hearts of men,
Who felt that Christ indeed had risen again.
Even the Jester, on his bed of straw,

憔悴的眼看见了荣美非同寻常，
他觉得里面有种从未经验的能力，
使他谦卑地跪在床前的地上，
他听到主急飘的衣裳，
拂过安静的空气升上天堂。

现在访问的时光已过，再一次
华蒙离去往多瑙河岸的回程，
那天使也再次踏上归家的路，
在途中展现他盛壮的扈从，
经过意大利的城和镇，
从沙莱诺港出海拔锚启碇。
再进入泊勒摩的城墙内，
升上他的宝座在伟大的朝廷，
听到修院传来祷告的钟声，
像是更美的世界在与我们交通，
他招呼罗波王近前来，
示意屏退其余的人众；
单独相对的时候，那天使问：
"你是王吗？"低垂着头，
罗波王的双手交叉当胸，
谦恭地回答："你最知道！
我的罪如同朱红；让我去
修院的静室好好忏悔，
跪爬在石头上，成为道路能到天庭，
赤脚行走，直到我负疚的灵魂赦净！"
那天使微笑着，从他光辉的脸上
圣洁的光照亮所有的地方，
听到邻近的教堂修士们诵唱，
传进敞开的窗，高越而嘹亮，
超越街道上市声的喧嚣扰攘：

With haggard eyes the unwonted splendor saw,
He felt within a power unfelt before,
And, kneeling humbly on his chamber floor,
He heard the rushing garments of the Lord
Sweep through the silent air, ascending heavenward.

And now the visit ending, and once more
Valmond returning to the Danube's shore,
Homeward the Angel journeyed, and again
The land was made resplendent with his train,
Flashing along the towns of Italy
Unto Salerno, and from thence by sea.
And when once more within Palermo's wall,
And, seated on the throne in his great hall,
He heard the Angelus from convent towers,
And if the better world conversed with ours,
He beckoned to King Robert to draw nigher,
And with a gesture bade the rest retire;
When they were alone, the Angel said,
  "Art thou the King?" Then, bowing down his head,
King Robert crossed both hands upon his breast,
And meekly answered him: "Thou knowest best!
My sins as scarlet are; let me go hence,
And in some cloister's school of penitence,
Across those stones, that pave the way to heaven,
Walk barefoot, till my guilty soul be shriven!"
The Angel smiled, and from his radiant face
A holy light illumined all the place,
And through the open window, loud and clear,
They heard the monks chant in the chapel near,
Above the stir and tumult of the street:

"他叫有权柄的失位，
　叫卑贱的升高！"
　在那诵唱以外有另一个韵律，
　升越像是单弦音在振荡：
　　"我是个天使，你是王！"

　罗波王，原来站在宝座的左近，
　举目看来，啊！只有他一人！
　所有的衣饰依然如旧，
　荣美的外袍缀玉绣金；
　当宫廷的侍臣来发现他在那里，
　跪在地上全心祷告，静默深沉。

"He has put down the mighty of their seat,
And has exalted them of low degree!"
And through the chant a second melody
Rose like the throbbing of a single string:
   "I am an Angel, and thou art the King!"

King Robert, who who was standing near the throne,
Lifted his eyes, and lo! he was alone!
But all apparelled as in days of old,
With ermined mantle and with cloth of gold;
And when his courtiers came, they found him there
Kneeling upon the floor, absorbed in silent prayer.

圣诞钟声

朗菲罗 Henry Wadsworth Longfellow

在圣诞节我听到了钟声，
奏出古老熟悉的歌颂，
　　甜美而且激越　反复地述说
地上有平安，善意归人群！
想到这日子又再来临，
普世欢腾和谐同庆，
　　钟楼传出钟声　歌唱持续不停
地上有平安，善意归人群！

一路来鸣钟，歌唱不断，
大地转动从黑夜到白天，
　　歌声乐音连连　旋律洪亮庄严
地上有平安，善意归人群！
可然后，从每个大炮黑色的口腔，
咒诅的雷声起自南方，
　　所发出的声响　淹没圣诞歌唱
地上有平安，善意归人群！

好像是强烈的地震发生，
撕裂了这大陆上许多家庭，
　　造成丧亡不幸　家门自相纷争
地上有平安，善意归人群！
在失望中我低头黯然，
说道："在这地上全无平安，
　　因为恨意深浓　在讥讽着歌颂
地上有平安，善意归人群！"

把钟声敲响更响亮更深妙：
"上帝没有死，他也不睡觉！
　　邪恶终必败亡　正义得胜昌旺
地上有平安，善意归人群！"

*此诗作于美国南北战争期间。

106

I heard the bells on Christmas Day
Their old, familiar carols play,

 And wild and sweet   The words repeat
Of peace on earth, good—will to men!
And thought how, as the day had come,
The belfries of all Christendom

 Had rolled along   The unbroken song
Of peace on earth, good—will to men!

Till, ringing, singing on its way,
The world revolved from night to day,

 A voice, a chime,   A chant sublime
Of peace on earth, good—will to men!
Then from each black, accursed mouth
The cannon thundered in the South,

 And with the sound   The carols drowned
Of peace on earth, good—will to men!

It was as if an earthquake rent
The hearth—stones of a continent,

 And made forlorn   The households born
Of peace on earth, good—will to men!
And in despair I bowed my head;
"There is no peace on earth," I said;

 "For hate is strong   And mocks the song
Of peace on earth, good—will to men!"

Then pealed the bells more loud and deep:
"God is not dead; nor doth he sleep!

 The wrong shall fail,   The right prevail,
With peace on earth, good—will to men!"

乡村铁匠

朗菲罗 Henry Wadsworth Longfellow

有个乡村的铁匠铺，
　　在一棵大栗子树旁；
那铁匠非常的强壮，
　　有双巨大有力的手掌，
满有筋肉褐色的臂膀，
　　像一束钢铁一样。

他的头发光亮，黑而且长，
　　脸面如同皮革皱纹；
眉梢流着诚实的汗珠，
　　尽可能地赚钱生存，
他面对全世界没有愧怍，
　　因为他从不亏欠任何人。

一周复又一周，从早到晚，
　　他风箱的声音可以听见；
你听到他挥动沉重的大锤，
　　击打节奏有时缓慢，
像管教堂的敲动那乡村的钟，
　　当夕阳低沉下山。

当孩子门放学回家
　　从那敞开的门张望；
他们爱看那炉中的火焰，
　　听那风箱吼叫的声响，
看到那迸起的火花，
　　像禾场上扬起的糠。

Under a spreading chestnut–tree
    The village smithy stands:
The smith, a mighty man is he,
    With large and sinewy hands;
And the museles of his brawny arms
    Are strong as iron bands.

His hair is crisp, and black, and long,
    His face is like the tan;
His brow is wet with honest sweat,
    He earns whate' er he can,
And looks the whole world in the face,
    For he owes not any man.

Week in, week out, from morn till night,
    You can hear his bellows blow;
You can hear him swing his heavy sledge,
    With measured beat and slow,
Like a sexton ringing the village bell,
    When the evening sun is low.

And children coming home from school
    Look in at the open door;
They love to see the flaming forge,
    And hear the bellows roar,
And catch the burning sparks that fly
    Like chaff from a threshing–floor.

主日他去到教堂，
　　坐在他儿子们的中央，
听牧师祷告和传讲，
　　听他女儿的歌唱，
在乡村诗班的歌声，
　　使他的心欢喜飞扬。

听来如同她母亲的声音，
　　歌唱在天上的乐园！
他不免又一次的想起她，
　　如何在坟墓里安眠；
泪珠流出了他的双眼，
　　就用粗硬的手擦干。

劳苦，欢乐，忧伤，
　　伴随着生命前进不止；
每早晨看工作开始，
　　每晚间看工作完毕；
有的事试去作，有的事成就，
　　他获得一夜的安息。

感谢，感谢你，我尊贵的朋友，
　　你所教导我们的课程！
在人生命的炼炉中，
　　我们的前途如此作成；
如此的在砧上锤炼又铸形，
　　每一燃烧的思想和行动。

He goes on Sunday to the church,
And sits among his boys;
He hears the parson pray and preach,
He hears his daughter's voice,
Singing in the village choir,
And it makes his heart rejoice.

It sounds to him like her mother's voice,
Singing in Paradise!
He needs must think of her once more,
How in the grave she lies;
And with his hard, rough hand he wipes
A tear out of his eyes.

Toiling,—rejoicing,—sorrowing,
Onward through life he goes;
Each morning sees some task begin,
Each evening sees it close;
Something attempted, something done,
He earned a night's repose.

Thanks, thanks to thee, my worthy friend,
For the lesson thou hast taught!
Thus at the flaming forge of life
Our fortunes must be wrought;
Thus on its sounding anvil shaped
Each burning deed and thought.

夜的颂诗

朗菲罗 Henry Wadsworth Longfellow

我听见夜的衣裾
扫过她大理石的殿堂！
我看见她黑貂皮的裙边
镶嵌着天上的星光！

我感觉到她的存在，大能的影响
俯在我以上；
夜平静，庄严地临在
像我所爱的一样。

我听见悲痛和欢乐的声音，
那多重的，轻柔钟铃，
充盈着那些夜所占领的房舍，
像是老年诗人的吟诵。

从午夜冷冽的水池
我的心灵畅饮憩息；
从那深池的泉源中
长久的平安涌流不止。

噢，圣善的夜，我学着接受
如同多人在我以前，
你把手指按在忧虑的嘴唇上，
他们就不再抱怨。

平安！平安！我发出奥莱斯迪的祷告！*
　　展开你宽阔的翅膀降临，
我所欢迎的，再三祈求的，最美的，
　　最爱的夜！

* 希腊神话：奥莱斯迪
(Orestes)为（Argos）王之子。
其母与情夫弑夫篡位。奥莱
斯迪逃亡，长成后归国，杀
母及情夫而复国为王。

I heard the trailing garments of the Night
Sweep through her marble halls!
I saw her sable skirts all fringed with light
From the celestial walls!

I felt her presence, by its spell of might,
Stoop o' er me from above;
The calm, majestic presence of the Night,
As of the one I love.

I heard the sounds of sorrow and delight,
The manifold, soft chimes,
That fill the haunted chambers of the Night,
Like some old poet' s rhymes.

From the cool cisterns of the midnight air
My spirit drank repose;
The fountain of perpetual peace flows there, –
From those deep cisterns flows.

O holy Night! from thee I learn to bear
What man has borne before!
Thou layest thy finger on the lips of Care,
And they complain no more.

Peace! Peace! Orestes–like I breathe this prayer!
Descend with broad–winged flight,
The welcome, the thrice–prayed for, the most fair,
The best–beloved Night!

孩童时间

朗菲罗 Henry Wadsworth Longfellow

当夜幕开始降下，
黑暗将接续白天，
一天事工完毕的休闲，
那叫作孩童时间。

我听到上面的房中，
有轻促的小脚步声，
有开房门的声响，
语音甜而柔轻。

从我书房的灯光可以看见
宽阔的楼梯上降下，
庄重的爱莉，嘻笑雅丽歌拉，
还有伊涤慈金黄的头发。

先是耳语，接着是安静：
但我知道从顽皮的眼睛，
他们在商议一同定计，
为要使我意外惊奇。
忽然间奔跑经过走道，
忽然间突击冲过厅堂！
这三道门都未曾设防，
他们冲进我堡垒的墙！

Between the dark and the daylight,

When the night is beginning to lower,

Comes a pause in the day's occupations,

That is known as the Children's Hour.

I hear in the chamber above me

The patter of little feet,

Tho sound of a door that is opened,

And voices soft and sweet.

From my study I see in the lamplight,

Descending the broad hall stair,

Grave Alice, and laughing Allegra,

And Edith with golden hair.

A whisper, and then a silence:

Yet I know by their merry eyes

They are plotting and planning together

To take me by surprise.

A sudden rush from the stairway,

A sudden raid from the hall!

By three doors left unguarded

They enter my castle wall!

他们爬上了我的角楼，
上了扶手和我的椅脊；
他们包围我无处可逃避，
好像他们遍处都是。

他们的亲吻几乎把我吞掉，
他们拥抱我交互缠绕，
叫我想起那滨镇的主教，
在莱茵鼠楼被群鼠所咬。

噢，蓝眼睛的强盗们，岂不想，
因为你们爬越了墙，
一个老胡子像我这样
哪能够同你们较量！

我紧困你们在我的城堡里，
绝不让你们逃奔，
要把你们放在牢狱中囚禁
在那圆楼里，我的心。

我要永远把你们放在那里，
是的，永远到一天，
到那墙壁变成颓垣，
与尘土一同归于衰残！

116

They climb up into my turret

O' er the arms and back of my chair;

If I try to escape, they surround me;

They seem to be everywhere.

They almost devour me with kisses,

Their arms about me entwine,

Till I think of the Bishop of Bingen

In his Mouse–Tower on the Rhine!

Do you think, O blue–eyed banditti,

Because you have scaled the wall,

Such an old mustache as I am

Is not a match for you all!

I have you fast in my fortress,

And will not let you depart,

But put you down into the dungeon

In the round–tower of my heart.

And there will I keep you forever,

Yes, forever and a day,

Till the walls shall crumble to ruin,

And moulder in dust away!

基督徒的呼召

卫里尔 John Greenleaf Whittier

不是常有旋风猛烈
像在可畏的何烈山，
不是常有焚烧荆棘的火焰
向米甸牧人的先知显现，
也不是那声音庄严
临到以色列的先知诗人，
也不是分岔火焰的舌头
也不是恩赐会说可畏的语言。

不常是有这些外表的记号
烈火和声音来自天上，
那神圣真理的信息
那从神来的呼召下降！
在人的心中觉醒
爱真实和公义，
热心追寻基督徒的理想
有力量去打基督徒的仗。

并不是限于男子汉的心房
才有这种神圣的影响，
妇女的心也能感觉到
超乎自己的温暖欢狂！
像那女人为救主奔走
在撒玛利亚的城墙，
像那些与热诚的保罗
跟谦和的亚居拉同工一样。

或像那些谦和的人殉道
成了罗马聚观的盛景，
或像那些在阿尔卑斯山的家乡
奋勇为十字军战争，

Not always as the whirlwind' s rush
On Herob' s mount of fear,
Not always as the burning bush
To Midian' s shepherd seer,
Nor as the aweful voice which came
To Israel' s prophet bards,
Nor as the tongues of cloven flame,
Nor gift of fearful words, –

Not always thus, with outward sign
Of fire or voice from Heaven,
The message of a truth divine,
The call of God is given!
Awaking in the human heart
Love for the true and right, –
Zeal for the Christian' s better part,
Strength for the Christian' s fight.

Nor unto manhood' s heart alone
The holy influence steals:
Warm with a rapture not its own,
The heart of woman feels!
As she who by Samaria' s wall
The Saviour' s errand sought, –
As those who with the fervent Paul
And meek Aquila wrought:

Or those meek ones whose martyrdom
Rome' s gathered grandeur saw:
Or those who in their Alpine home
Braved the Crusader' s war,

当沃德的青峦，颤动，听到，
传遍它死的幽谷，
使妇女们最后的残息
倾注出殉道者凯旋的歌声。

轻柔的，借着千般的事物
在我们的心灵上经过，
像和风抚过了细的琴弦，
或像云雾抚摸着草叶，
那乐音或是淡影，
留下奇异而新的记号，
对公义真实和恩慈的心灵
作出了轻柔的呼召。

噢，这样，如果些微真理和亮光，
闪过你等候的心间，
人类的需要缺欠，
展示在你心灵的眼前；
如果，为世人的忧苦沉思，
是你真诚的心愿，
不是为了你自己悲苦，
要使人欢乐缓释重担。

虽然全没有可畏的预报，
也没有外在的表现或记号；
虽然只有对里面的耳朵，
细语轻柔而声音微小；
虽然不可见，却是从天上来，
降落，只像是吗哪下飘，
像夜露无声，要好好留意
你天父爱的呼召！

120

When the green Vaudois, trembling, heard,
Through all its vales of death,
The martyr's song of triumph poured
From woman's failing breath.

And gently, by a thousand things
Which o'er our spirit pass,
Like breezes o'er the harp's fine strings,
Or vapors o'er a glass,
Leaving their token strange and new
Of music or of shade,
The summons to the right and true
And merciful is made.

Oh, then, if gleams of truth and light
Flash o'er thy waiting mind,
Unfolding to thy mental sight
The wants of human-kind;
If, brooding over human grief,
The earnest wish is known
To soothe and gladden with relief
An anguish not thine own; –

Though heralded with naught of fear
Or outward sign or show;
Though only to the inward ear
It whispers soft and low;
Though dropping, as the manna fell,
Unseen, yet from above,
Noiseless as dew-fall, heed it well, –
Thy Father's call of love!

伦敦教堂

浩屯伯爵 Lord Richard Monckton Milnes Houghton

在一个星期天的早上，
我站在一座教堂的大门旁，
会众都聚集在那里
还有几十部车辆
从车中走出一位贵妇
我常得有幸瞻仰。

她手持一卷公祷书，
还拿着饰金的香匣；
那书上清楚印着
人类救恩的徽记
但在十字架的上面
还有一顶镀金的冠冕 *。

一名谄媚的执事趋前
为她敞开了内门，
她的脚步仿佛是滑动，
轻盈的像在舞厅一般
在她邪恶的虚骄中
也许会有过一丝善念。

但在她后面来了一个妇人，
怀着渴慕向门里张望，
生活残酷的印痕，
刻划在她病弱的脸上
显示着悲惨的三合一
罪压，软弱，和痛伤。

她找不到空处安息和祷告，
早有人挤满了免费的座位 **；
与到处的盛装相比
她残破的外衣使她惭愧
"神的家容不下贫穷的罪人"，
她叹息着蹒跚的离开。

* 那金冠冕是勋爵的徽记。
** 英国教区的家庭，一般在教会中租定座椅，可迟到或不到，但别人不得坐用；其余的是免费自由座位(free seats)。

I stood, one Sunday morning,
Before a large church door,
The congregation gathered
And carriages a score, –
From one out stepped a lady
I oft had seen before.

Her hand was on a prayer–book,
And held a vinaigrette;
The sign of man' s redemption
Clear on the book was set, –
But above the Cross there glistened
A golden Coronet.

For her the obsequious beadle
The inner door flung wide,
Lightly, as up a ball–room,
Her footsteps seemed to glide, –
There might be good thoughts in her
For all her evil pride.

But after her a woman
Peeped wistfully within,
On whose wan face was graven
Life' s hardest discipline, –
The trace of the sad trinity
Of weakness, pain, and sin.

The few free–seats were crowded
Where she could rest and pray;
With her worn garb contrasted
Each side in fair array –
   "God' s house holds no poor sinners,"
She sighed, and crept away.

越过沙洲

丁尼生 Lord Alfred Tennyson

夕阳和夜星，
向我发出清晰的呼唤！
不要有沙洲呜咽的悲声，
当我出海航远。
但潮水似睡眠般的流动，
有太多的声响和浪花，
自无边无垠的深海涌来，
然后转而归家。

黄昏微光和暮钟，
随着来的是黑暗！
不要有送别的哀痛，
当我登舟扬帆；
超越时间和空间的界限，
海浪将我载去悠悠，
希望见我的舵手面对面，
当我越过那险阻的沙洲。

    1889 年，八十岁的丁尼生从英格兰的奥德沃茨(Aldworth)夏居，渡海到卫特岛(Isle of Wight)的冬季别墅去避寒。

    船过索伦(The Solent)海峡的沙洲，听到波浪冲激的呜咽声，似在悲泣，那是风暴将至的预报。安然抵达岛上，风暴才来到。

    几天后，丁尼生病了。雇来一个护士服侍，陪侍照顾衰老病中的诗人。在他们谈话时，那基督徒护士说："先生，您有很多诗作，但很少圣诗。您现在病中，我希望您写首诗，安慰其他病苦的人。"老诗人回想船过沙洲时的风浪声音，当夜在病床上写成了这首诗。诗中把沙洲的呜咽，用为丧葬的意喻。这虽然不是他最后的作品，但依他的嘱托，收为他每本诗集的最后一首。表明基督徒的生命之舟，胜过死亡面见救主耶稣基督的盼望。作者面对死亡没有惧怕，而是看到死亡后面的安息。他用平静近于渴望的心情，想象越过死亡的关栅，也就同时越过了官感的限制("bar""沙洲"，也有关限的意思)，而在肉体之外得见神(参伯一九：26/ 林前一三：12)，面见生命的"舵手"。

Sunset and evening star,

And one clear call for me!

And may there be no moaning of the bar,

When I put out to sea.

But such a tide as moving seems asleep,

Too full for sound and foam,

When that which drew from out the boundless deep

Turns again home.

Twilight and evening bell,

And after that the dark!

And may there be no sadness of farewell,

When I embark;

For tho' from out our borne of Time and Place

The flood may bear me far,

I hope to see my Pilot face to face

When I have crossed the bar.

失落的领袖

布朗宁 Robert Browning

1

只为了盈把的银钱他离开了我们，
　　只为了一条带子缀在他的衣裳，
发现幸运的赐予一度使我们伤心，
　　失去了对她别的恩惠的钦仰；
那些布施金子的更能够收买他，
　　使银子在他眼中失去了光芒；
我们供献的几文铜钱他哪还会在意！
　　高傲的心把紫衣当破布一样！
我们这批爱过他，跟过他，尊崇过他的，
　　曾生活煦育在他尊贵的，慈祥的眼光，
学习他伟大的语词，模仿他特有的调腔，
　　把他当我们的模式，不论生存或死亡！
莎士比亚是我们的，弥尔顿是我们的，
　　本恩斯，雪莱同着我们，他们从坟墓张望！
只有他，离开了改革的先锋队和自由人，
只有他下沉成为落伍者，同奴隶列行。

2

我们要前进兴旺　不需要靠他在场；
　　不用他的曲调　我们有诗歌激励歌唱，
事功仍然要作成　当他在夸口他的冥想，
　　我们偏依然静卧，让他去号令激扬；
勾销他的名字，记录下一个灵魂的失丧，
　　又一项事工的损失，又一条路径荒凉，
又一次人的堕落，又一次对神的侮辱！
　　又一次魔鬼的胜利天使的忧伤！
生命的暗夜开始了：请他不要再回到我们中间！
　　那里准会有疑惑，痛苦和彷徨，
借我们有名的颂赞，微光的昏黄，
　　不再是欢乐自信的晨光！
我们来教导他好好打一仗　英勇的攻击吧，
　　在我们征服他之前威胁我们的心房；
然后让他接受新知识且等我们，
　　先到主宝座前，得赦免进入天堂。

Just for a handful of silver he left us,

    Just for a riband to stick in his coat–

Found the one gift of which fortune bereft us,

    Lost all the others she lets us devote;

They, with the gold to give, doled him out silver,

    So much was theirs who so little allowed:

How all our copper had gone for his service!

    Rags – were they purple, his heart had been proud!

We that had loved him so, followed him, honoured him,

    Lived in his mild and magnificent eye,

Learned his great language, caught his clear accents,

    Made him our pattern to live and to die!

Shakespeare was of us, Milton was for us,

    Burns, Shelley, were with us–they watch from their graves!

He alone breaks from the van and the freeman

He alone sinks to the rear and the slaves!

We shall march prospering–not through his presence;

    Songs may inspirit us–not from his lyre;

Deeds will be done–While he boasts his quiescence,

    Still bidding crouch whom the rest bade aspire:

Blot out his name, then, record one lost soul more,

    One task more declined, one more footpath untrod,

One more devils' –triumph and sorrow for angels,

    One wrong more to man, one more insult to God!

Life's night begins: let him never come back to us!

    There would be doubt, hesitation and pain,

Forced praise on our part–the glimmer of twilight,

    Never glad confident morning again!

Best fight on well, for we taught him–strike gallantly,

    Menace our heart ere we master his own;

Then let him receive the new knowledge and wait us,

    Pardoned in heaven, the first by the throne!

那推动摇篮的手

华勒士 William Ross Wallace

赐福妇女的手！
天使护引它的力量和恩爱，
在王宫，村舍，茅屋，
啊，不论什么所在，
有彩虹温和地悬挂，
不受风暴的侵害，
因为那推动摇篮的手，
那手也掌管着世界。

婴孩是幼弱的泉源，
流出权力和美丽，
是母亲，首先引导那小溪，
活泼的灵魂从那里长起
长成善或长成恶，
流送阳光或流出暴力，
因为那推动摇篮的手，
那手也掌管着世界。

女人啊，你的使命多么神圣，
就在你自己的土地上！
保守，啊，保守那幼小的心，
时常向神的灵气开放！
是母爱缀成的珠串，
成为所有世代真实的奖章，
因为那推动摇篮的手，
那手也掌管着世界。

赐福妇女的手！
父亲们和儿女们呼求，
这神圣的歌声，
与天上的敬拜汇流
在那里没有风暴阴暗，
彩虹永远拱悬在上头，
因为那推动摇篮的手，
那手也掌管着世界。

Blessing on the hand of women!
Angels guard its strength and grace,
In the palace, cottage, hovel,
Oh, no matter where the place;
Would that never storms assailed it,
Rainbows ever gently curled;
For the hand that rocks the cradle
Is the hand that rules the world.

Infancy' s the tender fountain,
Power may with beauty flow,
Mother' s first to guide the streamlets
From them souls unresting grow--
Grow on for the good or evil,
  Sunshine streamed or evil hurled;
  For the hand that rocks the cradle
Is the hand that rules the world.

Woman, how divine your mission
Here upon our natal sod!
Keep, oh, keep the young heart open
Always to the breath of God!
All true trophies of the ages
  Are from mother–love impearled;
For the hand that rocks the cradle
Is the hand that rules the world.

Blessings on the hand of women!
Fathers, sons, and daughters cry,
And the sacred song is mingled
With the worship in the sky –
Mingles where no tempest darkens,
  Rainbows evermore are hurled;
  For the hand that rocks the cradle
  Is the hand that rules the world.

北国传奇：啄木鸟的故事

菲比·凯瑞 Phoebe Cary

在北地，遥远，遥远，
　　那里的日子白昼苦短，
冬夜有那么长的时间
　　他们不能够一直睡眠；
当冬天下雪的时候，
　　他们用迅捷的驯鹿拖雪橇；
孩子们像是小熊宝宝，
　　裹着多毛的皮裘看着可笑。

大人们说给孩子奇异的故事
　　我不相信那是真实；
但你可以学到功课，
　　且等我把这传奇告诉你。
从前，良善的圣徒彼得
　　还曾住在人间，
他走遍四方传道，
　　他所做的你也听见。

当他在地上周游旅行，
　　来到一个村舍的门口，
那里有个小妇人在做饼，
　　又放在炉火上烘烤；
那天他在禁食肚子饥饿，
　　一天已快过将近日落，
彼得向着她堆在那里的饼，
　　他并不多要只要一个。

她做了一个很小的饼，
　　放在炉中的炭火上，
她越看好像越大，

130

Away, away in the Northland,
  Where the hours of the day are few,
And the night are so long in winter
  That they cannot sleep them through;
Where they harness the swift reindeer
  To the sledges, when it snows;
And the children look like bears' cubs
  In their funny, furry clothes;

They tell them a curious story –
  I don't believe 'tis true;
And yet you may learn a lesson
  If I tell the tale to you.
Once, when the good Saint Peter
  Lived in the world below,
And walked about it, preaching,
  Just as he did, you know,

He came to the door of a cottage,
  In traveling round the earth,
Where a little woman was making cakes,
  And baking them on the hearth;And
being faint with fasting,
  For the day was almost done,
He asked her, from her store of cakes,
  To give him a single one.

So she made a very little cake,
  But as it baking lay,
She looked at it, and thought it seemed

要给别人那是休想。
因此她又再搓弄拚面，
　　做成了更小的一个；
当她端详着，再翻转，
　　跟从前做的同样太多。

她就再捏下很小一点面，
　　弄得菲薄压了又捻；
烤成像一片威化饼干
　　想到要给人犹不甘愿。
她想："我这饼似太小
　　如果我自己吃并不能饱，
但要给别人就太大了。"
　　所以把那饼在架上放好。

良善的圣彼得怒从心起，
　　他已经很饥饿以至发昏；
实在这样的一个妇人
　　足以惹得圣徒气愤。
他说："你太过于自私
　　不配穿人形住在人间，
给你有食物又有房屋，
　　并且有火给你保持温暖。
现在，你必须做筑巢的鸟，
　　你所得的食物定要微少，
要烦劳的啄，啄，啄，
　　每天啄那干硬的树壳。"
她立即穿过烟囱上升，
　　再也不能作人言人声，

Too large to give away.
Therefore she kneaded another,
  And still a smaller one;
But it looked, when she turned it over,
  As large as the first had done.

Then she took a tiny scrap of dough,
  And rolled and rolled it flat;
And baked it thin as a wafer –
  But she couldn' t part with that.
For she said, "My cakes that seem too small
  When I eat them of myself,
And yet too large to give away."
  So she put them on the shelf.

Then good Saint Peter grew angry,
  For he was hungry and faint;
And surely such a woman
  Was enough to provoke a saint.
And he said, "You are far too selfish
  To dwell in a human form,
To have both food and shelter,
  And fire to keep you warm.

"Now, you shall build as the birds do,
  And shall get your scanty food
By boring, and boring, and boring,
  All day in the hard, dry wood."
Then up she went through the chimney,
  Never speaking a word,

从屋顶飞出一只啄木鸟，
　　她已经变化成为鸟形。

只有她头上戴的那顶红帽，
　　仍然像从前一般，
其余的衣裳都被熏黑
　　像是炭和乌烟。
所有的学童来自乡间
　　都能够看见她在林中，
她住在树上直到今天，
　　啄着，啄食蛀虫。

这功课她教导我们学习：
　　人活着总不要单为自己，
免得你不可怜别人的缺欠，
　　有一天你自己要成为可怜。
所赐给你的要多多给予，
　　要听怜恤的呼召；
不要在你给予时看小为大，
　　你所接受的却以为是小。

我的孩子们，现在要记牢，
　　切莫忘行慈爱和良善，
当你看见啄木鸟的红帽，
　　和她穿的熏黑衣衫。
你可能不会给变成一只鸟，
　　即使你生活得自私不仁；
但你能够变得更微小
　　一个低鄙自私的小人。

And out of the top flew a woodpecker,
    For she was changed to a bird.

She had a scarlet cap on her head,
    And that was left the same,
But all the rest of her clothes were burned
    Black as a coal in the flame.
And every country schoolboy
    Has seen her in the wood,
Where she lives in the trees till this very day,
    Boring and boring for food.

And this is the lesson she teaches:
    Live not for yourself alone,
Lest the needs you will not pity
    Shall one day be your own.
Give plenty of what is given to you,
    Listen to pity' s call;
Don' t think the little you give is great,
    And the much you get is small.

Now, my little boy, remember that,
    And try to be kind and good,
When you see the woodpecker' s sooty dress,
    And see her scarlet hood.
You mayn' t be changed to a bird though you live
    As selfish as you can;
But you will be changd to a smaller thing–
    A mean and selfish man.

新巨像：自由颂

艾玛·拉撒路 Emma Lazarus

不同于那有名的伟大希腊铜像，

伸展着征服的膀臂达到各方；

在我们海浪冲溅的海口，对着夕阳

一个强壮的女人举着火炬发光

火焰是收蓄的闪电，她的名字是

被放逐者的娘。从她照引的手

向普世放出欢迎的光芒；

她慈祥地望着那长桥联结着双城形成的巨港。

"古老的土地，保留你们固有的堂皇！"

她静默的嘴唇喊着。"给我你的疲乏，贫民，

你拥挤的群众渴求呼吸自由舒畅，

你可怜的贱民在满集的岸上。

把这些无家的，风浪飘荡的人给我。

我擎着灯站在这金门！"

　　提起美国，有三个形象可以代表：纽约港口巍然屹立高举火炬的自由巨像，展翅的飞鹰和瘦削精明的生意人山姆叔。

　　美国南北战争之后，法国历史家 Edouard de Laboulaye 发起，由法国民间集资，经巴黎爱弗勒高塔的 Alexandre-Gustave Eiffel 设计，经雕塑家 Frederic Auguste Bartholdi 建造，于 1885 年完成，运来美国。像高 151 尺 1 寸，连座高约 305 尺，在 1886 年立于纽约港口移民入境经过的 Eliis 岛上。在像座的铜牌上，刻着艾玛·拉撒路"新巨像"诗的末五句。

　　美国女诗人艾玛·拉撒路(Emma Lazarus)，纽约人，于 1883 年写了"新巨像"诗，表达对美国收容难民慈爱精神的信仰与颂赞。

　　如果说"一幅图像胜过千言万语"，在这里我们看见了寥寥几行诗句，给巍然巨像注入了灵魂；这灵魂是基督教精神的具体表现。只有认识基督真理，才可以引人进入真理的光中。

Not like the brazen giant of Greek fame,

With conquering limbs astride from land to land;

Here at our sea–washed, sunset gates shall stand

A mighty woman with a torch, whose flame

Is the imprisoned lightning, and her name

Mother of Exiles. From her beaconed–hand

Glows world–wide welcome; her mild eyes command

The air–bridged harbor that twin cities frame.

"Keep, ancient lands, your storied pomp!" cries she

With silent lips.   "Give me your tired, your poor,

Your huddled masses yearning to breathe free,

The wretched refuse of your teeming shore.

Send these, the homeless, tempest–tost to me.

I lift my lamp beside the golden door!

天猎

汤仆生 Francis Thompson

我逃避他，历经白昼，到夜间；
我逃避他，历经年复一年；
我逃避他，历经我自己思念中
错综的迷径；在凄迷的眼泪里
我躲藏他，在连续的嘻笑后面。
我急速地攀登希望的远景，
又呐喊，流汗，
在下边巨大可怕的深渊，
那强壮的脚步，在身后跟着，跟在后边。
但不是匆忙的追赶，
脚步并不慌乱，
从容的速度，紧促而不失庄严，
脚步节奏中　声音响起
比那脚步更近：
　"你这背离我的，万有都背离你。"
我抗辩，逾越法制的边限，
有许多可爱的窗槛，垂着红的窗帘，
其间有恩爱的纠缠
(我虽知道他的爱跟随着，
却是深深的惧怕
唯恐有了他，就必须舍弃所有的其他爱恋)；
但是，如果那小窗扉只开启一扇，
他的狂风将冲进里面。
惧怕不知如何逃，爱却要追赶。
我奔逃，超越世界的边缘，
闯进了群星的金衢街道间，
扰乱了他们的栅栏寻求遮掩；
穿越那些芳香的瓶罐，
摇动月亮的银门发声铿然。
我对清晨说：快来；
告诉夜：不要迟延；

138

I fled Him, down the nights and down the days,
I fled Him, down the arches of the years;
I fled Him, down the labyrinthine ways
Of my own mind; and in the mist of tears
I hid from Him, and under running laughter.
Up vistaed hopes I sped;
And shot, precipitated,
Adown Titanic glooms of chasmed fears,
From those strong Feet that followed, followed after.
But with unhurrying chase,
And unperturbed pace,
Deliberate speed, majestic instancy,
They beat – and a Voice beat
More instant than the Feet –
"All things betray thee, who betrayest Me."
I pleaded, outlaw–wise,
By many a hearted casement, curtained red,
Trellised with intertwining charities
(For, though I knew His love Who followed,
Yet was I sore adread
Lest, having Him, I must have naught beside);
But, if one little casement parted wide,
The gust of His approach would clash it to.
Fear wist not to evade, as Love wist to pursue.
Across the margent of the world I fled,
And troubled the gold gateways of the stars,
Smiting for shelter on their clanged bars; Fretted to dulcet jars
And silvern chatter the pale ports o' the moon.
I said to dawn, Be sudden; to eve, Be soon;
With thy young skyey blossoms heap me over
From this tremendous Lover!

用你的新花掩埋我
躲避那极端的爱的眼！
撒出你朦胧的纱环绕我，叫他看不见！
我试遍他所有的仆役，终于发现
我虽然背逆他们却贞坚，
他们对主忠实对我却多变，
他们的违逆是真实，赤诚是欺骗。
我向所有速变的东西请求速援；
攀悬在每阵呼啸的风长鬣上面。
但不论他们如何猛驰，疾驶，
那碧蓝的长空平原；
或是乘驾雷电，他们紧附着他的车横越上天
绕蹄溅着飞行的电闪，
惧怕不知如何逃，爱却要追赶。
仍然不匆忙的追赶，
脚步并不慌乱，
从容的速度，紧促而不失庄严，
那脚步跟在后边，　语音比步声更加清晰
　"没有什么不接纳我，而能接纳你。"

我不再寻求从前的迷途
那脸孔是男或是女；
但仍然在小孩童的眼中
似乎有些什么，什么可以给我答复；
至少他们会支持我，一定支持我！
我转向他们满怀着希望，
可是，正当他们忽然示爱凝眸
将要把答案倾吐，
天使抓住了头发拉他们离去。
　"来吧，你们大自然另外的儿女，"
我说，"与我同享你们美好的欢娱，

Float thy vague veil about me, lest He see!
I tempted all His servitors, but to find
My own betrayal in their constancy,
In faith to Him their fickleness to me,
Their traitorous trueness, and their loyal deceit.
To all swift things for swiftness did I sue;
Clung to the whistling mane of every wind.
But whether they slept, smoothly fleet,
The long savannahs of the blue;
Or whether, Thunder–driven,
They changed their chariot ' thwart a heaven
Plashy with flying lightnings round the spurn of their feet –
Fear wist not to evade as Love wist to pursue.
Still with unhurrying chase,
And unperturbed pace,
Deliberate speed, majestic instancy,
Came on the following Feet,
And a Voice above their beat –
Naught shelters thee, who wilt not shelter Me."

I sought no more that after which I strayed
In face of man or maid;
But still within the little children' s eyes
Seems something, something that replies;
They at least are for me, surely for me!
I turned me to them very wistfully;
But, just as their young eyes grew sudden fair
With dawning answers there,
Their angel plucked them from me by the hair.
  "Come then, ye other children, Nature' s – share
With me," said I, "your delicate fellowship;

让我亲吻欢迎你，
让我与你拥抱轻抚，
嬉戏
弄我们母亲飘扬的长发，
欢宴
在她风为墙壁的宫府，
她湛蓝的顶盖遮覆，
照你纯洁的样子，
欢宴
在她风为墙壁的宫府，
她湛蓝的顶盖遮覆，
照你纯洁的样子，
从杯中，倾饮着
晶莹明亮的阳光。”
这些都过去了，
我曾是他们甘美团契中之一员
开启过自然的秘密之闩。
我知道一切的意含
在上天固执的脸；
我知道云如何升起
狂野的海喷吐沫涎；
所有的生或死亡
升或沉降　使他们能形成
我自己的心境，哀悼或逍遥
同他们欢乐或悲惨。
我很忧闷在晚间
当她燃点她闪亮的灯盏
围绕白昼死去的尊严。
我欢笑在清晨的眼帘。
我欢腾又悲哀随着气候变换，
天与我一同哭泣，

142

Wantoning
With our Lady–Mother's vagrant tresses
Banqueting
With her in her wind–walled palace,
Underneath her azured dais,
Quaffing, as your taintless way is,
Banqueting
With her in her wind–walled palace,
Underneath her azured dais,
Quaffing, as your taintless way is,
From a chalice Lucent–weeping out of the dayspring.?
So it was done;
I in their delicate fellowship was one –
Drew the bolt of Nature's secrecies.
I knew all the swift importings
On the willful face of skies;
I knew how the clouds arise
Spumed of the wild sea–snortings;
All that's born or dies
Rose and drooped with–made them shapers
Of mine own moods, or wailful or divine–
With them joyed and was bereaven.
I was heavy with the even,
When she lit her glimmering tapers
Round the day's dead sanctities.
I laughed in the morning's eyes.
I triumphed and I saddened with all weather,
Heaven and I wept together,
And its sweet tears were salt with mortal mine;
Against the red throb of its sunset–heart
I laid my own to beat,

天的甜泪和我的融合成咸；
夕阳的心赤红震颤
我把自己跳动的心并放在那边，
二者的热交会相连；但不是如此，
如此作，只是消除我人生的伤痛。
我的眼泪徒然沾湿了上天灰色的面颊。
噢！因为我们彼此言语不通，
我和自然界；虽然我言语有声
他们的言语却是静默，他们只是移动。
自然，可怜的继母，不能够舒解我的枯旱；
如果她还承认我，让她
解下那蓝色的胸衫，向我显露出
她双乳的柔软；
她从没有用一滴的乳汁滋润
我嘴唇的干渴。
逼近更逼近的追赶，脚步并不慌乱，
从容的速度，紧促而不失庄严，
有个声音传来的更快捷
在脚步的声响以先："注意，
如果不满足我，没有什么会满足你。"

我无助的等待你爱的下击！
一件一件的你解除了我的武装，
又打倒使我屈膝；
我全然无法反抗。
我想，我睡去，又醒觉，
慢慢地，我发现在睡中被剥脱得赤裸。
我曾卤莽的以充沛的青年精力，
在我撼动巨柱的时刻
尽情地任意生活；沾满了污迹，
我站在岁月堆积的灰尘里

And share commingling heat;

But not by that, by that, was eased my human smart.

In vain my tears were wet on Heaven's gray cheek.

For ah! we know not what each other says,

These things and I; in sound I speak–

Their sound is but their stir, they speak by silences.

Nature, poor stepdame, cannot slake my drouth;

Let her, if she would owe me,

Drop yon blue bosom–veil of sky, and show me

The breasts o' her tenderness;

Never did any milk of hers once bless

My thirsting mouth.

Nigh and nigh draws the chase,

With unperturbed pace,

Deliberate speed, majestic instancy;

And past those noised Feet–

A voice comes yet more fleet–

"Lo naught contents thee, who content'st not Me."

Naked I wait Thy love's uplifted stroke!

My harness piece by piece Thou has hewn from me,

And smitten me to my knee;

I am defenseless utterly.

I slept, methinks, and woke,

And, slowly gazing, find me stripped in sleep.

In the rash lustihead of my young powers,

I shook the pillaring hours

And pulled my life upon me; grimed with smears,

I stand amid the dust o' the mounded years–

My mangled youth lies dead beneath the heap.

My days have crackled and gone up in smoke,

我糟踏的青年死去沉埋在灰堆底。
我破碎的年日化成烟逝去，
如泡沫升涨又破碎在阳光下的水面。
是的，现在都已破失：梦幻
和作梦的人，琵琶和弄弦者；
超越我缀连幻想，在它编织的花样里
运转大地犹如小玩意在腕间，
腱索都嫌不够强健
因为地上沉重的忧伤过于充满。
啊！你的爱岂是
一种野草，虽则是不衰亡的野草，
不让任何花儿滋长只自己扩展？
啊！必定
无限的设计者，啊！
你岂是定要烧焦树林才可造成木炭？
我青年的力量耗尽抖颤着归于尘土；
现在我的心如同破裂的泉源，
眼泪从里面流积着，
从阴湿的思想不停地流
分溅在我心灵叹息的枝头。
既如此，又将如何？
果浆这样苦，果皮的味道何以堪？
我隐约的猜想迷雾中的时间朦胧难辨；
从永恒隐藏的城垣
却偶尔有号角声响起；
暂时震动迷雾闪开空隙一片，然后
在半瞥之后楼阙重被遮掩。
但到他传召之后
我才得看见，展现
绚丽的紫袍，柏叶的冠冕；
我知道他的名，号角已经宣示。

Have puffed and burst as sun—starts on a stream.

Yea, faileth now even dream

The dreamer, and the lute the lutanist;

Even the linked fantasies, in whose blossomy twist

I swung the earth a trinket at my wrist,

Are yielding; cords of all too weak account

For earth with heavy griefs so overplussed.

Ah, is Thy love indeed

A weed, albeit an amaranthine weed,

Suffering no flowers except its own to mount?

Ah! must—

Designer infinite!—

Ah! must Thou char the wood ere Thou canst limn with it?

My freshness spent its wavering shower i' the dust;

And now my heart is as a broken fount,

Wherein tear—drippings stagnate, spilt down ever

From the dank thoughts that shiver

Upon the sightful branches of my mind.

Such is; what is to be?

The pulp so bitter, how shall taste the rind?

I dimly guess what Time in mists confounds;

Yet ever and anon a trumpet sounds

From the hid battlements of Eternity;

Those shaken mists a space unsettle, then

Round the half—glimpsed turrets slowly wash again.

But not ere him who summoneth

I first have seen, enwound

With blooming robes, purpureal, cypress—crowned;

His name I know, and what his trumpet saith.

是否人的心或生命能出产
你的庄稼，你那产地
必须用粪肥和腐朽的死？
在那长久的追逐之后
巨响已近在身边；
那声音包围我像是突来的海涛一般：
"是否你的土地已全失尽
像破而又碎的瓦片？
看哪，因你逃避我，所有的都逃避你！
奇怪，可怜，无益的东西，
何必让其他的把你的爱隔离？
只有我从无有造出万有。"他说。
"人性的爱需要有人间的成就
你有什么可值得夸口
所有泥块的人中最肮脏的泥块？
唉，你不知道
你何等不值任何的爱！
你能找到谁肯救卑贱的你
除了我，除非唯一的我？
我把你拿去我剥夺
并非是要害你，
是要你能单从我手中寻得。
你一切童骏的误意
幻想是损失，我都已经为你收存在家里；
起来，握紧我的手，来！"

那脚步在我旁停住，
或许是我的阴与郁，
他的手荫伸出慰抚？
　"啊，最愚昧，最软弱，最盲目的，
我是那一位你寻求追逐！
你驱动我的爱，爱驱使我。"

　　汤仆生的诗，很像 17 世
纪英国宗教诗人的作品。在
"天猎"诗中，有丰富的意喻，
还像奥古斯丁 (St. Augustine)，
叙述自己的忏悔，特别是神的
恒久忍耐和不可抗拒的恩典。
人在神以外追寻满足，结果不
过是虚空和失望；也描述人的
逃避与神恩的追逐，仿佛是诗
篇第 139 篇的演述。Coventry
Patmore 称之为英国文学中的
最佳作品。

148

Whether man's heart or life it be which yields
Thee harvest, must Thy harvest fields
Be dunged with rotten death?
Now of that long pursuit
Comes on at hand the bruit;
That Voice is round me like a bursting sea:
　"And is thy earth so marred,
Shattered in shard on shard?
Lo, all things fly thee, for thou fliest Me!
Strange, piteous, futile thing,
Wherefore should any set thee love apart?
Seeing none but I makes much of naught," He said,
　"And human love needs human meriting,
How hast thou merited—
Of all man's clotted clay the dingiest clot?
Alack, thou knowest not
How little worthy of any love thou art!
Whom wilt thou find to live ignoble thee
　Save Me, save only Me?
All which I took from thee I did but take,
Not for thy harms,
But just that thou might'st seek it in My arms.
All which thy child's mistake
Fancies as lost, I have stored for thee at home;
Rise, clasp My hand, and come!"

Halts by me that footfall;
Is my gloom, after all,
Shade of His hand, outstretched caressingly?
　"Ah, fondest, blindest, weakest,
I am He Whom thou seekest!
Thou dravest love from thee, who dravest Me."

曲终人散

吉普霖 Rudyard Kipling

我们先祖自古信奉的神，
我们迤逦战线的主，
在他可畏的手覆盖下，
从棕榈到寒松的疆土；
主万军之神啊，还求与我们同在，
恐怕我们忘记　恐怕我们忘记！
喧嚣和呼喊静息了；
首领和君王都消逝；
谦卑和痛悔的心，
依然是你古老的祭。
主万军之神啊，还求与我们同在，
恐怕我们忘记　恐怕我们忘记！

远去了，我们的军舰消隐；
海屿和沙丘上的烟火低沉；
啊，我们昨天所有的煊赫
与尼尼微和推罗一同消尽！
万国的审判者，还求饶恕我们，
恐怕我们忘记　恐怕我们忘记！
如果眼前的权力使我们沉醉，
放肆的口舌对你失去敬畏，
像外邦人那样的夸口，
或像没有律法的贱坏，
主万军之神啊，还求与我们同在，
恐怕我们忘记　恐怕我们忘记！

因为外邦人的心所信托的
不过是烟囱和铁船壳，
看守，却不求你看守，
在尘土上建造所有尘土优越，
疯狂的夸张和愚昧的话语，
主啊，求你怜悯你的百姓！

先知诗人的 "曲终人散"

英国作家吉普霖心目中理想的殖民地政策，应该是宣扬福音，而不歧视本土文化；发扬英国声威，而不欺压弱小民族。这可称为罗曼蒂克福音思想。据说，他曾两次婉谢封授爵士勋衔，那是英国人的最高荣誉。

1897 年，英国女皇维多利亚在位六十年，全国举行钻禧庆祝，举世同欢。伦敦泰晤士报(London Times) 征请最有名的吉普霖，写一首诗。结果他写了 "Recessional"（圣职人员及诗班退席时唱的圣诗），并声明发表时及以后，都不接受任何报酬。

150

God of our fathers, known of old,
Lord of our far–flung battle–line,
Beneath whose awful hand we hold
Dominion over palm and pine –
Lord God of Hosts, be with us yet,
Lest we forget – lest we forget!
The tumult and the shouting dies;
The captains and the kings depart;
Still stands Thine ancient sacrifice,
An humble and a contrite heart.
Lord God of Hosts, be with us yet,
Lest we forget–lest we forget!

Far–called, our navies melt away;
On dune and headland sinks the fire:
Lo, all our pomp of yesterday
Is one with Nineveh and Tyre!
Judge of nations, spare us yet,
Lest we forget–lest we forget!
If, drunk with sight of power, we loose
Wild tongues that have not Thee in awe,
Such boasting as the Gentiles use,
Or lesser breeds without the law–
Lord God of Hosts, be with us yet,
Lest we forget–lest we forget!

For heathen heart that puts her trust
In reeking tube and iron shard –
All valiant dust that builds on dust,
And guarding, calls not Thee to guard –
For frantic boast and foolish word.
Thy mercy on Thy people, Lord!

那时，日不落的大英帝国，拥有举世无匹的海上霸权和历史上从没有过的最辽阔的疆土，真如日正中天。他竟然没想到讨什么人欢喜，写出来的诗，像是先知耶利米的信息，不是庆祝、颂扬，也不是感恩的话，却是祈求神的怜悯。其所表达的信息，是曲终人散，盛况过去，这激使国人批评，也使有些人深思。我们不知道，他到底是看见了什么异象，使他写出这样的诗章。但过了不到半个世纪，吉普霖的话应验了，日不落的大英帝国，竟然陨落了，往昔的兴盛，一去不返。

今天，无论什么国家，什么人，蒙神的恩典，叫你与人不同，仍然应该想一想："恐怕我们忘记"！

留守的牧人

盖瑞生 Theodosia Garrison

在乐园里的灵魂
并不是伟大也不是智慧，
但忠心的都有冠冕
每个人戴着无逊无愧。

我主人叫我在夜里看守羊群，
我的责任是坚守。我不知道
同工们在那大光里见到什么，
我不管那要他们去的语声，
我不知道他们是发狂或是惊惶，
我只知道我守住。
山坡上像是着了火；我感觉
翅膀从我头上面扫过；我跑去
看是否有什么危险惊吓了我的羊群。
虽然我看到他们仍然在圈里安卧，
虽然弟兄们哭泣又拉着我的衣袖，
我也不离开。

林中有盗贼，山上又有狼，
我的责任是留守。虽然有点怪，
我不想留住我的同伴，不愿
要他们待着跟我一同看守。
我没有听见他们所顺从的呼召；
我只知道我守住。

也许天亮时他们就回来，
报说伯利恒和他们去的原因。
我只知道独自在这里看守，
我知道一种奇异的满足。
我没有辜负那加在我身上的托付，
我别无所求——我守住。

152

There are in Paradise
Souls neither great nor wise,
Yet souls who wear no less
The crown of faithfulness.

My master bade me watch the flock by night;
My duty was to stay. I do not know
What thing my comrades saw in that great light,
I did not heed the words that bade them go,
I know not were they maddened or afraid;
I only know I stayed.
The hillside seemed on fire; I felt the sweep
Of wings above my head; I ran to see
If any danger threatened these my sheep.
What though I found them folded quietly,
What though my brother wept and plucked my sleeve,
They were not mine to leave.

Thieves in the wood and wolves upon the hill,
My duty was to stay. Strange though it be,
I had no thought to hold my mates, no will
To bid them wait and keep the watch with me.
I had not heard that summons they obeyed;
I only know I stayed.

Perchance they will return upon the dawn
With word of Bethlehem and why they went
I only know that watching here alone,
I know a strange content.
I have not failed that trust upon me laid;
I ask no more—I stayed.

The Shepherd Who Stayed:

大地和祭坛的神

柴思特屯 Gilbert Keith Chesterton

噢，大地和祭坛的神
请俯听我们的求告，
我们属地的统治者会动摇，
我们的人民漂移并死亡；
金墙成为埋葬我们的坟墓，
可耻的刀剑纷争，
不求你的震怒离开我们，
只求除去我们的骄傲。

从所有恐怖的教导，
从舌头和笔的虚谎，
从所有轻易的演讲，
叫残暴的人安康，
从出卖并妄滥
运用荣誉和刀，
从沉睡和咒诅中，
良善的主啊，释放我们！

用生命的绳索系住我们——
君王祭司和平民，
把我们所有的人捆在一起，
责打并拯救我们；
经历忿怒和欢喜
用信心和自由激励，
举起一个活的国家，
合成你唯一的剑。

O God of earth and altar,
Bow down and hear our cry,
Our earth rulers falter,
Our people drift and die;
The walls of gold entomb us,
The swords of scorn divide,
Take not Thy thunder from us,
But take away our pride.

From all that terror teaches,
From lies of tongue and pen.
From all the easy speeches
That comfort cruel men,
From sale and profanation
Of honor, and the sword,
From sleep and from damnation,
Deliver us, good Lord!

Tie in a living tether
The prince and priest and thrall,
Bind all our lives together,
Smite us and save us all;
In ire and exultation
Aflame with faith, and free,
Lift up a living nation,
A single sword to Thee.

守财者惊梦

司布真 Charles H. Spurgeon

夜来起狂风，
窗户皆震动。
守财奴陡然惊醒，
往复徘徊静室中。
转头看看背后，
边踱步，边颤惊。
查遍每道闩，每个锁，
探遍每个角落每条缝；
然后打开藏宝箱，
欣赏聚敛得意忘形。
蓦地良心猛省，
他搓着双手又捶胸。
他狂张着双眼，
罪咎的灵魂宣判发声：
大地若是保守那些矿藏，
我心深处也保得平安宁静；
但如今，品德已经卖空！
天啊，什么代价
　　　能补偿罪恶的伤痛？
噢，致命的黄金，引诱欺蒙，
人，软弱的人，
怎能战胜你的权能？
黄金从思想中赶走了荣誉，
只剩得一个虚名；
黄金在世上撒遍恶种，
黄金叫凶手去行凶；
黄金指引懦夫的心，
教他奸诈权术与败行。
邪恶多得谁能算清？
道德却在地上绝了影踪！

*司布真取材自 Austin's Chi-

ronomia

156

The wind was high,

The window shakes;

With sudden start,

The Miser wakes!

Along the silent room he stalks;

Looks back, and trembles as he walks!

Each lock and every bolt he tries,

In every creek and corner pries;

Then opens his chest with treasure stored,

And stands in rapture o' er his hoard:

But now with sudden qualms possest,

He wrings his hands, he beats his breast.

By conscience stung he wildly stares;

Thus his guilty soul declares.

Had the deep earth her stores confin' d,

The heart had known sweet peace of mind,

But virtue' s sold!

Good heavens! what price

Can recompense the pangs of vice?

O bane of gold! seducing cheat!

Can man, weak man, thy pow' r defeat?

Gold banished honour from the mind,

And only left the name behind;

Gold sow' d the world with every ill;

Gold taught the murderer' s sword to kill:

Twas gold instructed coward hearts

In treachery' s more pernicious arts.

Who can recount the mischiefs o' er?

Virtue resides on earth no more!

孩子们都已进来了吗？

侠名 Anonymous

夜晚临近时我常回想
那一幢老屋建在山上，
那庭院宽广百花绽放
孩子们自由的戏游欢畅。

深黑的夜终于降临，
欢笑也归于低沉，
母亲周围巡视并且问说：
"孩子们都已进来了吗？"

许多许多年已经过去，
那山上的老屋空庭
不再有孩子们的脚步响声
一切都寂静，那么的寂静。

但夜影伸展时我仍然看见，
虽然已经过了许多年，
我能够听到母亲的呼问：
"孩子们都已进来了吗？"

我在想，如果夜幕落下
地上最后的日子过完，
当我们跟外面的世界道别再见，
完全倦于我们儿时的戏玩。

当我们面见那位爱孩子们的主，
他受死救他们脱离罪苦，
我们是否听到他像母亲呼问：
"孩子们都已进来了吗？"

I think of times as the night draws nigh
Of an old house on the hill,
Of a yard all wide and blossom—starred
Where the children played at will.

And when deep night at last came down,
Hushing the merry din,
Mother would look all around and ask,
  "Are all the children in?"

' Tis many and many a year since then,
And the old house on the hill
No longer echoes childish feet
And the yard is still, so still.

And I see it all as the shadows creep,
And tho' many the years have been
Since then, I can hear my mother ask,
  "Are all the children in?"

I wonder if, when those shadows fall
On the last short earthly day,
When we say good—bye to the world outside,
All tired of our childish play,

When we meet the Lover of boys and girls
Who died to save them from sin,
Will we hear Him ask as Mother did,
  "Are all the children in?"

兄妹孤儿

佚名 Anonymous

我的马车到达乡村的旅舍，
　　最后余晖的夕阳
斜映着街对面古老的教堂，
　　把屋顶的风旗染上灿烂金黄。
为了打发晚餐前的时间，
　　我默默地踱过到对面，
在苔封的古老墓丛
　　寻味死者的遗愿。
那里许多寒素的青绿坟墓，
　　是贫困缺乏劳苦的安息之处；
也有许多诙谀的墓石，
　　表明他们曾拥有财富。

一棵凋落的槲树褐色的影子，
　　投射在一座坟是忧患的眠息，
在那里稀疏的草还未长起，
　　有两名褴褛的孩子坐着哭泣。
在当中放着一块面包，
　　他们二人都无意去取，
但他们看来是那么贫苦，
　　使我的心酸楚。
"我的孩子，对我来讲
　　为什你们这样的忧伤，
又为什浪费丢掉那面包，
　　会使许多人吃了欢畅？"

那小男孩，用可爱的语声回答，
　　眼泪成串的下滴：
夫人哪！我们在挨饿缺食，
　　即使有我们也不会任意抛弃。
"只是妹妹玛莉变得淘气，
　　我说好说歹她总不肯吃，
虽然我知道那面包实在是她的，

My chaise the village inn did gain,
Just as the setting sun's last ray
Tipped with refulgent gold the vane
Of the old church across the way.
Across the way I silent sped,
The time till supper to beguile,
In moralizing o'er the dead
That mouldered round the ancient pile.
There many a humble green grave showed
Where want and pain and toil did rest;
And many a flattering stone I viewed
O'er those who once had wealth possest.

A faded beech its shadow brown
Threw o'er a grave where sorrow slept,
On which, though scarce with grass o'ergrown,
Two ragged children sat and wept.
A piece of bread between them lay,
Which neither seemed inclined to take,
And yet they looked so much a prey
To want, it made my heart to ache.
  "My little children, let me know
Why you in such distress appear,
And why you wasteful from you throw
That bread which many a one might cheer?"

The little boy in accents sweet,
Replied, while tears each other chased,—
Lady! we've not enough to eat,
Ah! if we had, we could not waste.
  "But Sister Mary's naughty grown,
And will not eat whate'er I say,
Though sure I am the bread's her own,

因为她全天都不曾吃过东西。"
苍白瘦弱的玛莉说："肯定的，
　　除非亨利吃，我决不再吃半点，
因为昨天我吃过一点面包，
　　他什么都没吃打从前天。"

我的心膨胀，胸口起伏，
　　我感觉好像是无法言语；
静默地我坐在那坟墓，
　　把冰冷的小手用我双手握住。
所表现的忧苦是如此真实，
　　所表现传达了感恩的心意，
那抖颤的小男孩更挨近我，
　　说出了一个简单的故事：

在父亲离开我们以前，
　　他被坏人引诱去做海员，
妹妹和我不做一事只是贪玩，
　　我们家就在那大白杨树旁边。
但可怜的母亲时常哭泣，
　　眼看改变忒多，我形容不来；
她跟我们说不久就要死，
　　嘱咐我们要好好彼此相爱。
她说，也许我们会见到爸；
　　那天要等战争过去，
如果我们不能再见他，
　　上帝会做我们的父！
她同我们亲嘴然后死了，
　　我们就此不再有母亲；
有好多天我们坐着哭号，
　　一同在可怜母亲的坟。

For she has tasted none to—day."

  "Indeed," the wan, starved Mary said,

  "Till Henry eats, I ' ll eat no more,

For yesterday I got some bread,

He ' s had none since the day before."

My heart did swell, my bosom heave,

I felt as though deprived of speech;

Silent I sat upon the grave,

And clasped the clay—cold hand of each.

  "But when my father came not here,

I thought if we could find the sea,

We should be sure to meet him there,

And once again might happy be.

  "We hand in hand went many a mile,

And asked our way of all we met;

And some did sigh, and some did smile,

And we of some did victuals get.

  "But when we reached the sea and found

T was one great water round us spread,

We thought that father must be drowned,

And cried, and wished we both were dead.

  "So we returned to mother ' s grave,

And only longed with her to be;

For Goody, when this bread she gave,

Said father died beyond the sea.

  "Then since no parent we have here,

We ' ll go and search for God around;

Lady, pray, can you tell us where

That God, our Father, may be found?

虽然我们的爸不回家，

　　我以为在海上会把他找着，

在那里我们定能遇到他，

　　重聚在一起就会再快乐。

我们手牵着手走过许多里，

　　一个又一个逢人就问路；

有的人只微笑，有的人叹息，

　　也有人给我们一些食物。

但我们到海边的时候才发现，

　　原来是一片无边大水汪洋，

想来父亲必然已经淹死，

　　哭着，恨不得我们也都死亡。

因此，我们回到妈的墓上，

　　只希望能跟她在一块；

好姨来给我们这些干粮，

　　说是爸已经死在海外。

既然在这里我们没有父母，

　　我们要去到处寻找上帝；

夫人，求你，能不能告诉我们

　　那位上帝，我们的爸，他在哪里？

我们的妈说，上帝在天上，

　　好姨说，那也是妈的所在；

所以如果妈知道我们需要他帮忙，

　　我想，她或许要他到这里来。

我拉紧这两个孩子在我胸前，

　　哭着说：来吧，你俩，跟我同住；

我要做你们第二个母亲，

　　给你穿，给你吃，给你安息照顾。

上帝仍然是你们的父亲，

　　是他的恩典差我到这里，

教导你们好顺从他的旨意，

　　引导你的脚步，使你的心欢喜。

With looks of woe too sadly true,
With looks that spoke a grateful heart,
The shivering boy then nearer drew,
And did his simple tale impart:

  "Before my father went away,
Enticed by bad men o' er the sea,
Sister and I did naught but play,—
We lived beside yon great ash—tree.

  "But then poor mother did so cry,
And looked so changed, I cannot tell;
She told us that she soon should die,
And bade us love each other well.

  "She said that when the war was o' er,
Perhaps we might our father see;
But if we never saw him more,
That God our father then would be!

  "She kissed us both, and then she died,
And we no more a mother have;
Here many a day we' ve sat and cried
Together at poor mother' s grave.

  "He lives in heaven, our mother said,
And Goody says that mother ' s there;
So, if she knows we want his aid,
I think perhaps she ' ll send him here."

I clasped the prattlers to my breast,
And cried, "Come, both, and live with me;
I' ll clothe you, feed you, give you rest,
And will a second mother be.

  "And God shall be your Father still,
T was he in mercy sent me here,
To teach you to obey his will,
Your steps to guide, your hearts to cheer."

古列王陵墓

佚名 Anonymous

雄伟的巴比伦发起了举哀，
里底亚的大理石宫殿深沉地回应；
如同遥远海洋波澜被风吹送，
哈马丹城的高墙遍起哀声。
因为他，那可畏的裁判者，新兴帝国的倚恃，
常胜的雄鹰之子，伟大，睿智，公义，
亚述著名征服的剑，玛代王者的能力，
最终在更高权能的手下低头着地。

黑暗忧伤遍满地上，幼发拉底河蜿蜒流过，
银色波浪的底格里斯河，听到了挽歌；
从广阔和炎热的东方，到冰封的北国，
小鼓和竖琴都静默，号啕的悲声遍野。
那里有一座孤独的坟墓，杂草繁生，
只一棵弯曲的可怜棕树靠近苔封的墓碑，
缓慢的微风，一阵阵穿过树间叶丛，
好像为下面长眠的人，叹出丧曲的低喟。

旁边荒野的喷泉溅起点点泡沫；
田田浮水的红莲平静地发出芬芳，
野土狼偷偷出来寂静孤单的搜索；
潜伏的山狐狸在兀鹰巢旁隐藏。
这荒野的安息处竟成为勇者的卧床？
荣耀的道路，启发盛名的光，竟到此尽头？
君王中建树最高者，威名传播远方，
为何你可夸的名遗忘，荣光的星黯然而收！

就近看铭刻的诗文如何说？"啊，人的虚骄！
宇内可羡慕的礼物曾属我，大地的颂赞毫不吝惜。
旅行的人，如果恳求者的回声在你心头响起，
啊，莫嫉妒这一抔土掩盖我必朽的躯体安息！"

* 古列王常译居普士。史载：亚力山大东征过此墓，沉思良久，挥手令继续前进。末二句意："旅人啊！当年曾不乏人求恩乞怜，今唯愿此遗躯入土为安！"

166

A voice from stately Babylon, a mourner's rising cry,
And Lydia's marble palaces give back their deep reply;
And like the sounds of distant winds o'er ocean's billows sent,
Ecbatana, thy storied walls send forth the wild lament.
For he, the dreaded arbiter, a dawning empire's trust,
The eagle child of victory, the great, the wise, the just,
Assyria's famed and conquering sword, and Media's regal strength,
Hath bowed his head to earth beneath a mightier hand at length.

And darkly through a sorrowing land Euphrates winds along,
And Cydnus with its silver wave hath heard the funeral song;
And through the wide and sultry East, and through the frozen North,
The tabret and the harp are hushed,– the wail of grief goes forth.
There is solitary tomb, with rankling weeds o'er–grown,
A single palm bends mournfuly beside the mouldering stone
Amidst whose leaves the passing breeze with fitful gust and slow
Seems sighing forth a feeble dirge for him who sleeps below.

Beside, its sparkling drops of foam a desert fountain showers;
And, floating calm, the lotus wreathes its red and scented flowers,
Here lurks the mountain fox unseen beside the vulture's nest;
And steals the wild hyena forth, in lone and silent quest.
Is this deserted resting–place the couch of fallen might?
And ends the path of glory thus, and fame's inspiring light?
Chief of a progeny of kings renowned and feared afar,
How is thy boasted name forgot, and dimmed thine honour's star!

Approach,what saith the graven verse? "Alas for human pride!
Dominion's envied gifts were mine, nor earth her praise denied.
Thou traveller, if a suppliant's voice find echo in thy breast,
O, envy not the little dust that hides my mortal rest!"

167

后语：圣经文学与失落的瑞兽

好多年前，我们住在奥立根州的撒冷。小城静居，是一段难忘的日子。

住在我们隔壁，是一个白人医生，夫妇有四个孩子。他们是我所遇到最没有种族成见的人。有一次，他们郑重说："如果不是因你们年纪还轻，我们想叫孩子们称你们爷爷奶奶。"

这位医生，每周一晚上有聚会，同几个医生和学者，讨论鲁益师(C.S. Lewis)的作品和达尔文的进化论。那是以不信者为对象的聚会。曾邀我同去。可惜，我对达尔文缺乏兴趣，而对鲁益师的作品，也未全读过，所以不曾参加。他妻子则是很活跃的反堕胎运动主席；他们家还收容着小未婚妈妈，待产后安置母子的生活问题。他们夫妇都是热心的天主教徒。

有一天，谈话中间，我笑着说："我也是 catholic〔指宇宙性的教会〕，小写的'c'。"然后，转而问那丈夫："恐怕你也会 protestant 吧？小写的'p'，对某些事持反对意见吧？"他回答说，反对神甫独身制度。

我问那太太说："你怎会成为天主教徒呢？"因为我知道她生在密其根州 Grand Rapids，那地方福音派教会很强。她说："我们家本来是浸信会的，住在教会附近。我小的时候，去教堂练钢琴。那里的牧师很势利眼，看不起我们，对我们态度很坏。母亲就决定离开那里。"当然，现在他们的孩子们，也跟着进了天主教。我虽然没说："卿本佳人，奈何作贼！"但显然福音派教会，失去这样的花，怎能不感慨？又是一个可悲的故事。可能他们的感受，不一定会跟实际相同。

鲁益师这位英国文学家，曾任教于牛津和剑桥大学，有约二十五本著作，包括学术性的作品，灵修作品，还有科学小说和童话，诗歌和散文，都是有深度，有影响力的好书。也许，一般人能够写出任何一本这样的书都该满足。但影响最深的，好像还是他的童话。

鲁益师的特点，是他对圣经有精深的认识，而后能用浅明的笔法，把其精义表现于所写的作品。这是圣经文学的极高境界，能达到广大的群众。1998 年，鲁益师诞生一百周年，英国还为他发行纪念邮票，可见其如何受国人重视。就以他的童话诗"迟来的搭客"来说吧。

西洋神话里的"独角瑞兽"，仿佛中国传说的麒麟，只是头顶当中，有一只红颜色螺旋角，是直的，其身体跟马相似，尾巴像狮子，全身白毛，紫头，蓝眼；象征贞洁。当然，现在绝种了。但在许多家庭里，常见陈列着这种微塑型。孩子们会问起，为什么现在的动物园中没有？且听鲁益师叔叔道来。

迟来的搭客

C.S.Lewis (1898—1963)

雨声急密，天空低沉而阴暗，
诺亚的儿子们站在方舟的窗前。

群兽都进来了，但雅弗说："我见还有一种兽，
在那门前直叩；迟来了，孤独无偶。"

含说："让它去叩门吧，任它淹死或练游泳，
看看我们的情形吧，这里已经是无处可容。"

闪说："它仍在叩门呢，拼命叩着焦急惊惶，
它四蹄像独角那样的坚硬，却遍体带着异香。"

含说："莫做声，你如果惊醒老爹来看
是什么在门外，准会增加我们的工作负担。"

从下面的暗处，传来诺亚的高声大吼，
"有活物在叩门！放它进来再关闭方舟。"

含高喊回应，猛力戳那两兄弟不让做声：
"那不过是雅弗，他在用锤敲下一支鞋钉。"

诺亚说："孩子们，我听到像是马的蹄声。"
含说："噢，那是可怕的豪雨敲击着屋顶。"

诺亚仓皇地爬上顶层，探头一看出去；
他的脸转灰青，双膝发软，撕自己的胡须，

"看，看！它不再等了。它离去，逃脱。
儿子们，今夜，你们合伙，真干了绝活！

"就算我能赶过它，它也不会再转回
我们对它不客气，自然赢得人家鄙视不理会。

"啊，高贵的孤兽，我的儿子们真不友好，
如此的黑夜你何处能寻得棚舍和草料？

"啊，那金的蹄，啊，飘洒的长鬃，翕张的鼻孔
充满气愤！啊，那弯弓的倔强颈项，可爱的傲性！

"啊，要多么长久，在人的心上留下犁沟
要多久，它才会再度来到棚舍和槽头？

"我们的种类要经历漫长的黑暗弯曲路径，
像茎枝折断的花，颓丧的垂头度过人生，

"含啊，全世界要以生你的那日子可诅可咒，
为了你，竟在方舟启航时失落那独角瑞兽。"

　　孩子们从诗中听到的悲惨故事，是独角瑞兽被关在诺亚方舟的门外，也许可以教导他们爱护动物，不要使现在的动物绝种。但是，对成人也颇有可以深思的教训：方舟代表基督的救恩，除他以外，别无拯救。可惜，有些人像主耶稣所责备的文士和法利赛人，"当人前把天国的门关了，自己不进去，也不容别人进去"(太二三：13)。但另一种，也同样的不负责任：在教会的围墙里面，自己进了天国，却全然不关心别人，又自私懒惰，像诗中诺亚的儿子们，把别人关在天国的门外。
　　世界上许多文学作品中，都有洪水的记载。在圣经中，方舟是预表基督。世人都犯了罪，结局是审判和灭亡。唯一的救法，是相信进入基督里面："除他以外，别无拯救，因为在天下人间，没有赐下别的名，我们可以靠着得救。"(徒四：12) 这首诗的主旨，是鼓励人及时传福音，趁着今天是拯救的日子，引人进入方舟。最好

是在孩子的时候。

蒙田(Michel de Montaigne, l533—1592)极力主张及早教育儿童："趁泥土柔软的时候，现在，现在赶快在急速旋转的轮子上，做成器皿。"这个叙事诗，正是借说故事，教导儿童注意传福音。更特别的，全诗没有说教性的劝勉，却启发孩子们自己省思。

我们可以从挪亚的话看出，独角瑞兽是罕见的，有其品格和个性，不是恋栈豆的驽马可比。驽马只要有得吃就行；瑞兽却是一经拒绝，掉头就走，不会轻易再来。所以从小养成尊重别人，是非常重要的。

也是鲁益师说过：我们在世上所遇到的，没有普通的人；不是要在永世里得荣耀，荣美无比，就是要在地狱里，永远受羞辱，可厌至极。这正是但以理书的话(但一二：2)。如果我们看到这么重要，就该努力得人，不要因外貌而失人。

知道传福音的重要，我们该对为何传福音没有疑问。从这里，进一步想到如何传的问题。从鲁益师的实在例子，可以知道，文学作品是一个不可忽略的工具。所以，不要把基督教文学，当做是少数人的兴趣，是冷门艺术；而该认识是每个信徒可以做的事，当做的事。

可惜，相当多的人，拒绝踏进礼拜堂，对听讲章不表示兴趣；但他们不拒绝读好的文学作品。而且报章刊物，会帮助我们刊载，传播；教育机构会在教科书中采用，帮助我们推广；社区会传诵；不用说，教会和家庭中，都该时常提倡谈论。这样，基督教文学就有前途，可以使人得救恩，也可进一步而改变文化。

让我们多读圣经，多注意读基督教文学，而写作基督教文学，要写出基督教文学的杰作。

附"迟来的搭客"

The Late Passenger

The sky was low, the sounding rain was falling dense and dark,
And Noah's sons were standing at the window of the ark.

The beasts were in, but Japhet said, "I see one creature more
Belated and unmated there come knocking at the door."

"Well let him knock," said Ham, "Or let him drown or learn to swim.
We're overcrowded as it is; we've got no room for him."

"And yet it knocks, how terribly it knocks," said Shem, "Its feet
Are hard as horn—but oh the air that comes from it is sweet."

"Now hush," said Ham, "You'll waken Dad, and once he comes to see
What's at the door, it's sure to mean more work for you and me."

Noah's voice came roaring from the darkness down below,
"Some animal is knocking. Take it in before we go."

Ham shouted back, and savagely he nudged the other two,
"That's only Japhet knocking down a brad-nail in his shoe."

Said Noah, "Boys, I hear a noise that's like a horse's hoof."
Said Ham, "Why, that's the dreadful rain that drums upon the roof."

Noah tumbled up on deck and out he put his head;
His face went gray, his knees were loosed, he tore his beard and said,

"Look, look! It would not wait. It turns away. It takes its flight.
Fine work you've made of it, my sons, between you all tonight!

"Even if I could outrun it now, it would not turn again—Not now.
Our great discourtesy has earned its high disdain.

"Oh noble and unmated beast, my sons were all unkind;
In such a night what stable and what manger will you find?

"Oh golden hoofs, oh cataracts of mane, oh nostrils wide

With indignation! Oh the neck wave—arched, the lovely pride!

"Oh long shall be the furrows ploughed across the hearts of men
Before it comes to stable and to manger once again,

"And dark and crooked all the ways in which our race shall walk,
And shriveled all their manhood like a flower with broken stalk,

"And all the world, oh Ham, may curse the hour when you were born;
Because of you the Ark must sail without the Unicorn."

C.S. Lewis (1898–1963)
English novelist, essayist, and educator
Author, The Screwtape Letters and The Chronicles of Narnia

附：诗人简介

莎士比亚（William Shakespeare,1564—1616）
英国剧作家，诗人。

约翰·但恩(John Donne ,c. 1571—1631)
英国诗人，伦敦圣保罗大教堂首牧。

塞利(James Shirley ,1596—1666)
英国剧作家，诗人，教师。

乔治·赫柏特(George Herbert, 1593—1633)，
英国形式派诗人。

生于显要世家。三岁时，其父选为院士，受任大学
发言人，显示颇有政治前途。1624 年，当选国会
议员。但对政治兴趣淡泊。1627 年母丧，谢绝政
治。1630 年，受任乡村教会牧师。他一生敬虔，
十七岁时，立志专写宗教诗篇，成《圣殿诗集》。

弥尔敦 （John Milton ,1608—1674）

英国最著名清教徒诗人，并散文作家，兼擅拉丁文及英文。1649 年英国内战，清教徒国会军推翻王室，克伦威尔执政，弥尔敦任拉丁秘书，相当于外交部长。1652 年双目失明，由马卫勒助理。1660 年，英王复辟，得当时任国会议员的马卫勒尽力援救，免于入狱。1665 年，其长诗《失乐园》完成，初为十卷，于 1667 年出版(1674 年增至十二卷出版)。其后《得乐园》及其另一杰作史诗《斗士参孙》完成于 1671 年。

布莱斯翠(Ann Bradstreet, c.1612—1672)

美国最早的女诗人。

其夫曾任新英格兰总督。

贝克斯特(Richard Baxter, 1615—1691)

英国清教徒教牧及作家。曾任克伦威尔军牧。

英王查理二世复辟后，曾因非国教立场而数次入狱。

文涵(Henry Vaughan, 1621—1695)

英国诗人。在南威尔斯行医。自称受敬虔的乔治·赫柏特影响归正。

马卫勒(Andrew Marvell, 1621—1678)

英国形式派诗人。

于克伦威尔执政期间，任弥尔敦拉丁秘书助理，相当于外交次长。英王查理二世复辟后，选为国会议员。弥尔敦因曾参加清教徒革命，并著文指斥查理一世为叛国暴君，主张处以死刑(1649)，为新政府不容，议以监禁；马卫勒极力营救庇护。

肯恩(Thomas Ken, 1637—1711)

英国教牧，圣诗作家。

肯恩正直敢言，曾为主教，并英王查理二世宫廷牧师。讲道时，常当英王面指责宫廷淫佚奢侈等罪恶。但查理许为诤友。后为主教。因不肯对英王威廉及玛莉妥协，得罪当权者，于1691年去职入狱。获释后在贫困中安度二十年去世。在任温彻斯特学院院长时，为鼓励学生祷告写了祷告手册，其中载有早晚的祷告诗，"赞美真神"每篇的结束，成为今天教会通行的"三一颂"。

奚波(Colley Cibber, 1671—1757)

英国演员兼剧作家。

1730年，被举为"桂冠诗人"，但为当世文人所鄙。为之长诗主角。

坡仆(Alexander Pope, 1688—1744)
英国诗人，擅讽刺诗。幼年生病致发育不正常，体弱，但写作甚多，并翻译《荷马史诗》。

德怀特(Timothy Dwight, 1752—1817)
美国教牧，教育家，诗人。为美国神学家爱德务滋之外孙，曾任耶鲁大学校长。其孙同名亦任耶鲁神学教授及校长。

克莱比(George Grabbe, 1754—1832)
英国诗人。

昆瑞·亚当斯(John Quincy Adams, 1767—1848)
曾任美国第六任总统(1825—1829)。其父约翰·亚当斯为美国第二任总统(1797—1801)。昆瑞·亚当斯卸任后，为国会众议员(1831—1848)。有人问他，以曾任总统之尊，而屈为议员，是否降格？他说："服务国家，无论任何职务，都不是卑下的。"这首"人之欲"讽世诗，仿佛是现代的传道书，指出一切都是不足轻重的，真正的需要是指神的怜悯。

177

孟歌马利(James Montgomery, 1771—1854)

苏格兰诗人，报纸编辑。

巴屯(Bernard Barton, 1784—1849)

英国诗人。

拜伦(Lord George Gordon Byron, 1788—1824)

英国浪漫诗人。

雪莱(Percy Bysshe Shelley, 1792—1822)

英国浪漫诗人。

菲莉雪·海门斯(Felicia D.Hemans,1793—1835)

英国诗人。

178

济慈(John Keats, 1795—1821)

英国浪漫诗人。

习医但从未执业。因病往意大利，逝于罗马。

珀斯 （Caroline Bowles）

19世纪英国诗人。

威廉·诺克司(William Knox)

19世纪美国诗人。

莫锐斯(George Pope Morris, 1802—1864)

美国报纸编辑，诗人。

爱默生(Ralph Waldo Emerson, 1803—1882)

美国哲学家，诗人，论文作家。

浩屯伯爵 (Lord Richard Monckton Milnes Houghton, 1809—1885)

英国诗人，文学赞助者，也是提倡教会改革的人。

朗菲罗 (Henry Wadsworth Longfellow, 1807—1882)

美国诗人，教育家。

卫理尔 (John Greenleaf Whittier, 1807—1892)

美国诗人，从早年自学，爱文学，是极为敬虔的 Quaker 传道人，强烈反奴役的领袖。

丁尼生 (Lord Alfred Tennyson, 1809—1892)，

英国桂冠诗人，作品很受时人欢迎，得到"人民诗人"的雅号。

布朗宁 (Robert Browning, 1812—1889)

英国诗人，剧作家。

华勒士(William Ross Wallace, 1819—1881)
美国诗人。

非比·凯瑞(Phoebe Cary, 1824—1871)
美国诗人。

艾玛·拉撒路(Emma Lazarus, 1849—1887)
美国诗人，论文作家，慈善家。
为援助受迫害的犹太人，组织救济团体。

汤仆生(Francis Thompson, 1859—1907)，
英国诗人，父亲执业医生。父亲希望他读神学，但他选
择习医学。不过，习医失败，贫病交迫，为止病痛，又
染上了鸦片的嗜好，沦落伦敦街头，卖火柴和报纸为
生，一度寄居在修鞋店里帮闲。但他总执意不肯放弃所
喜爱的文学和鸦片。后来，有一个编辑发现了他的才
华，在其杂志上发表了他的诗，并送他入医院疗养恢复
健康，又助他刊行诗集。他的诗出版后，勃朗宁读过之
后大为赞赏。

盖瑞生(Theodosia Garrison, b. 1874)

美国诗人。

吉普霖(Rudyard Kipling, 1865—1936)

英国作家，诗人。

二十岁即有文名，著有多本小说及诗集。在二十七岁时，英国认为是拜伦以后第一人。1907 年成为第一个获得诺贝尔文学奖的英国人。

柴思特屯(Gilbert Keith Chesterton, 1876—1936)

英国新闻作家，评论家。